The DORSET
Weather Book

by Mark Ching and Ian Currie

Quiet lanes and rolling downland, open heaths and a spectacular coastline beloved by geologists. These are some of Dorset's virtues. So are the novelist Thomas Hardy and the ancient stronghold of Maiden Castle. Not so well appreciated is the great variety of the county's weather. The wild windiness of Portland contrasts with the often soft effusive airs blowing across the sub tropical gardens of Abbotsbury. Huge waves can buffet the Cob at Lyme Regis whilst hardly a ripple stirs in Poole Harbour. In winter rain is more likely to fall at Weymouth but high up on the lofty heights around Shaftesbury deep snow can lie for days and even months as in 1963.

Dorset can sometimes lie in the battle zone between the blustering temperate Atlantic winds and an icy blast from Siberia. This can generate a classic blizzard as in 1881 or 1978 when snow drifts of over 12 feet blocked roads and railways and cut off villages for a week or so.

In summer cooler Atlantic air can meet hot breezes from southern Europe and monumental thunderstorms may arise. It is no coincidence that Dorset holds the national record for the greatest daily fall of rain. On 18th July 1955 a series of thunderstorms yielded a mighty 11 inches of rain at Martinstown. This amounted to over half London's rainfall for that year.

Some of the storms have generated powerful vortexes and one tornado on 5th June 1983 sucked up hundreds of pieces of coal and coke high into a thundercloud near Wareham and then bombarded houses and gardens with a rain of carbon further east in Poole and Bournemouth.

Dorset is not a wet county. The district around Weymouth compares favourably with places further east in Sussex and Kent but in the hilly areas to the north west around Beaminster as much as ten to 12 inches of additional rain can often be added to the yearly total.

The Dorset coast is a regular contender for a place at the top of the sunshine league. Annually as much as 2100 hours of bright sunshine has beamed down on Swanage, Poole, Weymouth and Bournemouth in years such as 1911, 1959 and 1990. The temperature soared to 95F in the summer of 1990.

The weather is never out of the news for long and some years have been particularly eventful. The snowy winters of 1947 and 1963; the blazing summer of 1976; the great gales of 1987 and 1990 and the autumn floods of 1960 continue to provoke poignant memories amongst Dorset folk. Bad weather is not confined to the twentieth century as the storms of 1824 and 1703 illustrate.

This book provides a fascinating insight into the ever changing moods of our weather. It details all the main weather events for each of the past 100 years presenting a unique and illustrated county record. In spite of these terrible events Dorset must still be regarded weatherwise as one of the most favoured of English counties. Many thousands of holiday-makers who flock to its beaches and places of outstanding natural beauty each year bear witness to this and so does the meteorological data.

Trying to go to work, February 1978.

ISBN 0 9531603 0 0

First Edition December 1997
Copyright © 1997 by Frosted Earth
No part of this publication may be
reproduced or stored in a retrieval
system, or transmitted in any form or
by any means, electronic, mechanical,
photocopying, recording or otherwise
without prior written permission of
the copyright owner.

Published by Frosted Earth
77 Rickman Hill,
Coulsdon,
Surrey CR5 3DT
Tel: 01737 554869

Acknowledgements

Arthur Grant, Ken Ayres, Ben Cox and Staff Blandford
Museum, Barry Cox Hon. Librarian R.N.L.I. at Poole.
Particular thanks to Ian Murray Editor Bournemouth Daily
Echo and staff Anne Dickie, Sally Amess, Scot Harrison and Joanna
Codd, Ted Braunhholtz, Brian Bugler, Bridport Museum Service,
Ron Brown, British Rainfall, Climatological Observers Link,
Dorset Advertiser Series, Mrs Dicker, Dorset County Museum,
Dorset County Museum, Dorchester, Dorset County Record Office,
The Dorset Natural History and Archaelogical Society, Hampshire
and Isle of Wight Weather Book, David Haysom Curator
Tithe Barn Museum and Art Centre Swanage, Margaret
Jeffrey, Journal of Meteorology, Fran Lockyer, A. S. Lord,
Lyme Regis [Philpot] Museum, J.R. Oliver, Mary Payne, P.E.
& M.E. Payne, Meteorological Magazine, Mrs Richards,
Curator Portland Museum, Royal Meteorological Society,
Staff at Bournemouth Reference Library, Staff at Dorchester
Reference Library, Suart Dapp, Stuart Morris, Reg Vincent,
Weymouth and Portland Dept.of Leisure, Entertainments
and Tourism, Western Gazette Newspaper.

Photographic Credits

Front cover: Swanage Station February 1990, Ken Ayres;
Back cover: Portland Bill, September 1993, Fran Lockyer;
Dorset County Museum, Dorchester, Dorset: pages 3 top, 6, 8,
12, 17, 18, 22, 25, 34, 39 bottom, 40 top, page 41 bottom, page
42 bottom, 47, 59, 60, 61, page 64 top. page 65; Ian Currie
collection: pages 3 bottom, 14, 16, 21, 22 bottom, 83, 92, 95;
Lyme Regis [Philpot Museum] Museum print page 9;
Blandford Forum Museum Trust page 11; Bridport Museum
Service: pages 12 top, 38 bottom, 39 top, page 40 bottom,
page 42 top, page 45 top, 53; Tithe Barn Museum and Art
Centre Swanage: pages 15 top, 25 bottom, 27, 28; By permission of Weymouth and Portland Borough Council
Museum Services: pages 15 bottom, page 41 top; Ken Ayres:
pages 33, 48, 70, page 90 bottom; Mark Ching: 36, 38 top, 79,
80, 93; Bournemouth Daily Echo: Southern Newspapers
PLC: pages 2, 26, 31, 44, 45, 50, 55, 66, 67,71, 74, 75, 76, 77,
81, 82, 84, 85, 86, 87, 88, 89, page 90 top; Western Gazette:
page 72; Mr A.S. Lord: 49; P.E. and M.E. Payne pages 53, 58;
Fran Lockyer: 54, 73; Mr Stuart Morris:page 56, 57 bottom;
Reg. Vincent: page 56 top; Ron Brown: pages 63; Debbie
Brown: page 69; Brian Bugler page 64 bottom; Ted
Braunholtz: page 91.

Front cover: Swanage Station February 1990, by Ken Ayres

Back cover: Portland Bill, September 1993, by Fran Lockyer

Printed by Litho Techniques (Kenley) Ltd.
46-50 Godstone Road, Whyteleafe, Surrey CR3 0EA
Telephone. 0181 668 7573

Two Moods of Dorset's Weather

June and July 1909 did little to tempt one to the beach being cool and wet but conditions relented in August especially in the second week and these children made the most of it at Weymouth.

Storms breaking on Chesil Beach.

THE COUNTY OF DORSET

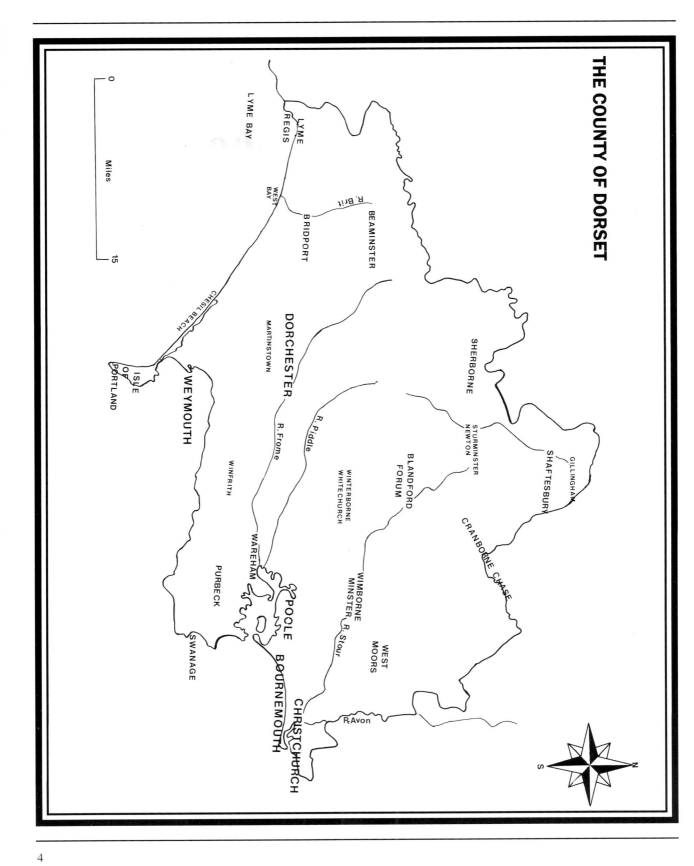

The boat that was launched on both sides of Chesil.

Measurements in Imperial – see page 93 for conversion chart.

1703

After midnight on the 26th November befell arguably the greatest storm of the millennium with various estimates of between 8,000 to 15,000 deaths, mostly at sea. They included the builder of the Eddystone Lighthouse Henry Winstanley. He was on the reef at the time with his workmen putting some extra touches to the overly ornate and somewhat impractical structure. It even included an elegant stateroom and splendid gilded bed chamber. After the storm not a stanchion of the building remained nor were there any survivors.

At Christchurch an account by William Mitchell spoke of twelve sheets of lead on the church roof "rouled up together, that 10 men could not have done the like, to the great amazement of those that saw 'em". A house was blown down in Puddletown and ten shillings was paid to overseers towards the cost of repair. Near Shaftesbury trees were blown down in diverse directions and the windows of the church were damaged. Throughout southern England over 400 windmills were demolished.

1709

At Sherborne an inscription at the Abbey of a great hailstorm on 16th May reads thus: "This Monument erected by Mr Thomas Mansell of this Towne in Remembrance of a Great Hailstorme May 16th. AD 1709 between the hours of one and four in the afternoon which stopping the course of a small River West of this Church caused of a sudden and Extraordinary flood in the Abbey-garden and Green; running with so rapid a stream that it forc'd open the North Door of the Church displaced and removed about 1,222 foot of the Pavement and was 2 foot and 10 inches high as it passed out at this South-Door."

1816

Snow lay on the ground from 12th April to the 15th and the summer that followed was disastrous for its harvest, known as "the year without a summer". The appalling weather was possibly the result of an eruption during the previous year of Mount Tambora when 36 cubic miles of rock and dust were hurled high into the upper atmosphere veiling the sun and causing a worldwide drop in temperature.

1824

The Rector of Wyke Regis, George Chamberlain, described a terrible tempest on 22nd November 1824: "The village of Chisel was nearly destroyed, twenty-six of the Inhabitants drowned, and upwards of eighty Houses damaged or washed down by a tremendous Surf which broke over the Chisel Bank, and bore everything away with irresistible violence before it. This awful visitation was occasioned by a heavy Gale, which, happening at a Spring tide and commencing from the South South East, increased till eight o'clock, when it blew a most dreadful Hurricane, such as never had been known before in the memory of Man … The sea ran down the Streets of Chisel with a sufficient depth of water to float a vessel of a hundred tons burden: and the Wrecks of the Houses, with the furniture of the poor Inhabitants, were every where strewed upon the Shore. The Ferry house leading to Portland was washed away, and the Ferry Man drowned. The communication between the Island and the Mainland was nearly destroyed by the ravages of the Sea, which carried away the Sand Bank on the Eastern Side, and rendered the passage four times wider than it was before … The pier of Weymouth Harbour was materially damaged, and three fourths of the Esplanade at Melcombe Regis entirely thrown down and demolished … The same Storm destroyed the Church at Fleet, and threw down several houses … The Colville West India Man of four hundred tons burden was totally wrecked in the West Bay, and every Soul on board perished, besides several minor wrecks too numerous to mention."

Governor John Penn launched a national appeal and gifts were received from around the country including the King who donated £200. Stuart Morris's book *Portland – An Illustrated History* described the donated clothing such as 34 waist coats and drawers; 100 pairs of men's stockings; 177 linsey and stuff petticoats; 232 shifts; 55 bonnets and 70

Shaftesbury is one of the snowiest places in Dorset set high up on the edge of a 700 foot plateau overlooking the Blackmoor Vale. The year 1886 was very snowy and this picture of Salisbury Street shows the aftermath of a heavy snowstorm.

This scene at Godmanstone in mid November 1894 shows the result of three weeks of relentless rain with parts of Dorset receiving as much as a foot of rain. One lad has found a novel way to avoid getting his feet wet.

babies' frocks and caps etc.

One of the most tragic incidents that befell the people of Portland in this dreadful storm was the death of Richard Best, the ferryman mentioned in Chamberlain's account. He had some 30 years' experience of weather and tide at the ancient ferry of Smallmouth the only link between the island and the mainland until 1839. He struggled to save a horse and was swept away and drowned. When the storm had abated the Passage House, ferry boat and posts were destroyed and the channel width was four times its former size.

Another grim tale was of a woman who lost her new born baby torn from her arms. She herself was fortuitously thrown into a boat and as she passed a house she was pulled in by young Tom Mitchell from an upper window. The rubble from collapsed houses was still visible into the twentieth century.

The storm wrecked at least ten vessels along the coast with much loss of life. However one craft had a bizarre experience. The 70 ton sloop *Ebenezer* lost her mainsail and a boy and the master were drowned. Three other hands clung on to the seemingly doomed storm-lashed vessel as she headed shorewards. Massive waves swept her up onto the crest of Chesil Beach and the islanders managed to secure it. There she remained for three months before being caulked with tar and pitch and then hauled over the beach and refloated on the east side into the Roads, one of only two vessels to have been both landed and launched on both sides of Chesil!

The storm was also very severe at Lyme Regis. A rogue tide surpassed high water five hours before expected. It rose above the west wall of the Cobb and breached it costing £13,000 to repair. An old man and his wife spent the entire 'hurricane' in the Cobb's pounded buildings and yet somehow survived.

The vessel *Unity* foundered at Lyme and drifted along the coast towards Charmouth and stuck under Black Ven where Capt Bennett effected an heroic rescue saving the crew. Another ship, *The Reserve Cutter*, was washed seawards and two men on board were drowned.

1875

A downpour of rain on the 14th July in Lyme Regis brought ruin to agriculture. Damage to hay and in places wheat was immense. Whole fields of grass hay were washed away and to the west the Axe valley in Devon was submerged.

1879

Snow fell in April and winter was still evident well into May. June and July were both very wet and August was unfavourable to farmers with the highest rainfall for 65 years. It proved the most disastrous season of the century for agriculturists. At Wimborne there was a great loss of bees.

1881

The Great Blizzard of 18th/19th January was said to have caused more hardship in the county than had ever been known.

1890

A great flood at Whitsun, 25th May, when the River Lyn came roaring through Lyme Regis. Rain gauges in the town overflowed but 3.7 inches was measured by an observer at Holm Cleve.

An ox was roasted on the ice at Sherborne Castle during the coldest December of the nineteenth century. The wind blew from the chill northeast at Hazelbury Bryan on 23 days.

1891

At Hazelbury Bryan Rectory the Rev Cannon Wheeler recorded no rain at all during the month of February and he described it as "so bright and spring-like that it could have been mistaken for the merry month of May". But one familiar saying is especially apt for spring weather, "few things are more certain than the unexpected". A tremendous snowstorm commenced at about 11.45am on the 9th March and continued incessantly until midday on the 10th. The fine crystalline snow was driven in the face of a tremendous gale into huge drifts up to 15 feet deep. It was very reminiscent of the great blizzard of January 1881.

A wedding had to be postponed at Loders Church because the bride was unable to travel to the ceremony. The snow even settled amongst the church bells at Blandford muffling their tones.

A remarkable feat was achieved by the postmaster at Blandford who, despite the raging snowstorm, managed to drive his cart pulled by three horses to Sturminster Newton and return the same evening. In Litton Mr Pitcher, a baker, employed several men at three shillings a day including food to deliver loaves to his customers.

The railway line from Dorchester to Weymouth was so completely blocked that the formidable array of a snow plough and four engines failed to force a passage through. Near Spetisbury five engines were snowbound, a singular sight.

A labourer was found almost buried in the snow at Winfrith and succumbed to exposure shortly afterwards. A telegraphic report from Cerne Abbas read "the six sided crystals hold sway at present over humanity. Business at a standstill, drifts 10 to 15 feet deep."

The cause of such severity was a deepening depression which moved northeast from Biscay. Bitterly cold easterly winds blew in its circulation. Further afield a train called the "Zulu Express" left Paddington Station, London at 3pm on Tuesday afternoon of the 9th and finally limped into Plymouth at 8.30pm on the 13th, having been immersed in an enormous snowdrift near Okehampton. On Dartmoor the gorge-like valley of Tavey Cleave was reported to be filled to a depth of 300 feet.

1894

Between 23rd October and 16th November 12.84 inches of rain fell at Maiden Newton including four consecutive days with over an inch from the 11th November. Heavy rain fell quite widely in southern England causing deep floods. Furniture swum about in people's basements in Weymouth whilst boats plied the streets. Residents were marooned in their houses in Swanage.

1895

February was an extraordinary month being rainless at Wimborne Minster but bitterly cold and the weather station run by the Reverend G. Billington recorded a mean temperature of 28.1F making it one of the coldest months of the nineteenth century. Bournemouth's lowest temperature on record of just 11.2F was measured during this month.

1896

A droughty summer felt especially north of Gillingham with the failure of the root crop after having had virtually no hay in May. At Winterborne Steepleton only 0.14 inches of rain fell in 46 days up to 1st June. This was the fourth such exacting summer for farmers in six years.

1897

Rainfall was above average up to the end of August in Mudeford by 6.38 inches, March being particularly wet. The valley of the Avon was mostly under flood water from February to the middle of April. However many observers remarked how fine and still October was.

1898

An astonishing snowstorm began late on Monday 21st February when earlier in the day it had been almost springlike. The winter so far had been quite open with scarcely any frost. Then, with the barometer falling rapidly, rain turned to snow and fell all night long in a veritable cascade accompanied by lightning and intermittent peals of thunder. By next morning it lay fully 16 inches deep at Dorchester and

13 inches at Wimborne. The snow was very adhesive and caused enormous damage to telegraph and telephone fittings. Wires were festooned across roads. Strong tubular iron poles were bowed in a grotesque manner.

In Winton many trees were bent almost double with the weight of snow and branches of pines littered the roadways. Many conservatories had their glass stoved in by the sheer weight of snow. In Poole a lady was knocked down and bruised by an "avalanche" tumbling from a roof at New Street.

1899

After a somewhat backward spring June set the pattern for a fine summer. There were 13 cloudless days. An observer at Christchurch remarked of July "delightful weather throughout, brilliant skies and splendid nights as a rule". In Bournemouth from 1st July only half an inch of rain was measured over the next 58 days.

For the most part the serene weather continued throughout September and October, the latter having an excess of 49 hours of sun. There was an exception for east Dorset during the early hours of 6th September when just over two inches of rain fell accompanied by vivid lightning and loud thunder. Roads and basements were flooded in Bournemouth and the lower pleasure gardens were submerged. Lightning struck houses in Grove and Stewart Roads. At Bere Regis the storm was described as severe and a small apple tree which was surrounded by trees of much larger girth and height was struck.

February 1895 was an ideal skating month being bitterly cold but dry and bright. The residual water from the heavy autumnal rains of 1894 has frozen and skating abounds on East Meadow, Fordington, on the edge of Dorchester.

When eight million tons plunged to the sea

Farm cottages on the verge of collapse in the mighty Landslip of 1839 near Lyme Regis.

THE superb cliff scenery around Lyme Regis is well known by holidaymakers and especially liked by fossil hunters. The cliffs towering over 300 feet look motionless and solid against the elements. But seen on a stormy day they seem less than permanent and particularly west of Lyme Regis nature has conspired to lend a helping hand for shales and limestones are precariously overlain by chalk and greensand. Rain water permeates through these but not through the shales rendering the whole mass unstable.

In 1839 the summer was wet and the rain continued at frequent intervals through the autumn and early winter amounting to twice the average with numerous gales driving the water into cracks and fissures.

On the 23rd December fractures developed in the ground around Dowlands Farm a few miles west of Lyme Regis and labourers' cottages began to crack, doors would not open and a trackway started to subside. These incidents were a prelude to one of the greatest landslips ever to befall the coastline of Britain.

On Christmas night two coastguards were on duty in the neighbourhood and it was whilst battling against a strong gale as they walked along the cliff top that one of them jammed his leg into a fissure. As the moon shone around them they could see the land cracking and heaving in every direction accompanied by a sound like "the tearing of cloth". Two other men were on duty at Culverhole Point when they saw the sea violently agitated with a dark ridge rising in the water. Rocks crashed in a cacophonous confusion and they told of "flashes of fire and a strong smell of sulphur".

The grey light of dawn revealed a new cliff 210 feet high with a huge chasm in front some 20 acres in area, the result of eight million tons of cliff subsiding. In amongst the jumbled mass of rocks there was a patch of land tilted but intact on which stood hedges and fields of turnips and corn unscathed.

The dark ridge seen rising in the water was a reef which was previously ten feet under water. It had been thrust 300 to 500 feet seaward of the former high water mark and was now raised in places to 40 feet above the sea. A lagoon had been formed at one end enclosing a natural harbour.

The Great Victorian Blizzard

AFTER a week of intensely cold weather with ice covering Weymouth Harbour in the early hours of Tuesday 18th January a furious blizzard began. The snow was not the fleecy flakes generally seen but small hard granular ice crystals blown with such a force by a violent northeast gale that it was blasted through the smallest gaps in window frames, doors and under roof tiles. The sand-like snow penetrated through the most minute interstices. The screaming tempest abruptly awoke those in slumber, many with their beds smothered in snow. Even ceilings collapsed as attics filled with the icy shards.

Anybody venturing abroad could barely make any progress and had to be well wrapped against the snow that rasped the face like a desert sandstorm. A traveller benighted in the county looking out on the dawn would have thought he had arrived in an Arctic region rather than the sunny south of England.

In Bournemouth according to one witness "the gale blew a perfect hurricane and the view of the sea from the cliffs and pier was as awful as it was grand". An observer at Christchurch measured snow a level three feet, from Sherborne an average depth of two feet. From all parts of the county the same message was manifest, all traffic was halted. No such block of human business, no such closing up of everyday life had occurred in living memory.

At Sturminster Newton a train was literally buried in a drift. Four trains were brought into Wimborne by three powerful engines with a snow plough in front, the snow was banked up higher than the train itself.

Postman Stoodley strove to get under way on his round from Weymouth Post Office which on a good day would take eight hours. He battled his way through countless snowdrifts before collapsing and was found unconscious beside the Dorchester Road. He was carried to an inn and fortunately recovered. Henry Hawker was not so lucky. He died near Thorncombe immersed in a deep drift in sight of his cottage. Two children died trying to walk from Hamworthy to Morden. They were found entombed in huge drifts.

Conditions along the coast were tempestuous. In the roadstead at Weymouth an American barque rammed the Channel Island steamer, the *Aquila*, setting her adrift and she in turn carried away the entire length of a landing jetty and played havoc with the quay.

Even though Lord Justice Bagally and Mr Justice Lopes arrived for the Winter Assize at Dorchester the session did not start for neither the grand jurymen, petty jurymen nor witnesses could reach the town. The High Sheriff, Mr W.R. Banks, took 19 hours to travel 20 miles trudging half the distance on foot.

Cattle and sheep died in their hundreds and thousands of men were out of work and it was said that there was more hardship in Dorset than had ever been known. Even in London's Oxford Street there were reports of snow drifts ten feet deep.

In Dorchester soup kitchens were set up. For one penny the poor who queued were to be given a quart of soup and a small loaf. Weymouth was even more charitable providing free sustenance to the penniless.

To complete the Arctic appearance of the countryside the northern lights [Aurora Borealis] shimmered in the night skies towards the end of the month.

THE GREAT SPRING DROUGHT OF 1893

Notes from Dorset Observers

Christchurch	Only 0.01 inches of rain in 58 days 18th March to 14th May. No rain for 42 consecutive days.
Corfe Castle	From 2nd March to 21st June only 1.11 inches in 112 days.
Winterbourne Steepleton	Hay crop an entire failure.
Gillingham	Almost total loss of hay. Spring corn scanty. Store stock at times unsaleable.
Bridport	A field of wheat in sheaf on 3rd July.
Lyme Regis	Only 1.99 inches in four months – believed to be unique in this part of the country.
Swanage	From 28th February to 23rd June less than one inch of rain.
Poole	On 26th April relative humidity only 28 per cent.

Two scenes from Blandford after the Great Blizzard of 1881.

West Street, Bridport, March 11th 1891, after the Great Snowstorm.

The aftermath of the fierce March 1891 snowstorm taken at Shaftesbury on March 11th. Note the roof blown bare of snow, the massive drifts in the lee of the hedge and the path trodden by the cottagers on the edge of the blocked lane.

Meteors, whirlwinds and muddy rain

1900

At Sherborne in February severe flooding occurred when a foot of snow melted in a rapid thaw onto still frozen ground but July brought some hot weather which triggered thunderstorms. Two men were struck by lightning at Chickerell near Weymouth. One was on the top of a hay cart whilst another was holding an iron bar. Both survived.

In a wet year the 30th December was particularly sopping as over England as a whole a cubic mile of water fell as a depression moved east from the Bristol Channel to Dover. This would fill up the bodies of water in the Lake District four times over. At Wimborne Minster 2.45 inches of rain fell and the month's total reached 7.45 inches at Beaminster.

1901

Although a dry year with only 26.41 inches of rain falling at Buckhorn Weston a mammoth 2.9 inches of rain was recorded at Winterborne Herringston on the 14th August in just ten hours with hardly a breath of wind. Meanwhile earlier in the summer hailstones three inches in circumference were reported from Sherborne.

1902

On the 3rd January the air pressure reached 30.93 inches [1047 mb] at Bournemouth.

A beautiful, bright, crimson sun pillar seen just after sunset in the Bournemouth area on the 6th March. It was caused by sunlight being refracted by thin high level ice cloud. It was a dry year and at Wimborne Minster rainfall was short by 6.1 inches.

A waterspout was observed from the cliffs between Osmington and Winfrith during July.

1903

The third week of February brought an extraordinary fall of dust and muddy rain. In Bournemouth fog had a lurid glow to it whilst elsewhere rain water when collected looked like it had been mixed with milk or flour. Windows were coated with a yellow silt.

On the 25th October what was described as a strong whirlwind travelled from Wareham through Kingston Lacy, Stour, Stanbridge and Uppington and thence on to Horton and Woodlands to the north of Wimborne Minster. Damage was estimated at being over £1,000 in Gaunts Park alone. Some 50 yards of hedge were torn out of the ground and at Horton eight magnificent elms were shattered. As in common with many whirlwinds or tornadoes damage was limited to a path no more than 100 yards in width.

October was a very wet month with rain falling on every day at Beaminster and the yearly total, 49.25 inches, was ten inches above the average.

1904

After the previous sodden year and a wet January and February with 10.8 inches of rain at Beaminster an observer at Upwey stated that underground water was exceptionally high. However the autumn was very dry so that by the end of December levels were very low.

1905

A remarkable barometric reading on the 28th January in the Poole-Bournemouth area of 31.02 inches [1050 mb]. Severe frosts in late May did great damage to fruit, potatoes and the frost was mentioned as being very sharp at Gillingham.

1906

At Wimborne two months, January and October, accounted for nearly half the yearly rainfall of 34.47 inches. July, August and September were very dry.

Snow fell in North Dorset around 10pm on Christmas Day.

1907

The northern lights or the Aurora Borealis were seen from Shaftesbury on the 9th February.

September was described by many as a perfect month being dry, warm and sunny and it was ideal for gathering in the harvest. However the contrast in October was remarkable. For instance at Wimborne September measured 0.44 inches of rain whilst October measured a soaking 10.54 inches with similar values at Lyme Regis, the latter having its wettest October since the station opened in 1882.

1908

Remarkable snow storms took place on 24th-25th April. Depths were up to a foot. Over England it probably represents a record for the time of year. The spectacle of newly sown fields knee deep in snow and trees in leaf bent to the ground with their icy accumulations was a bizarre sight. At Sturminster Marshall four inches of snow was on the ground at 9am on the 24th and by 11am it had increased to eight inches.

An extraordinary localized deluge affected the Portland and Weymouth areas on 18th to 21st October inclusive. On Portland 9.34 inches was measured and it was estimated that a phenomenal 6.89 inches fell in just five hours on the 21st at the southern tip of Portland Bill.

December supplied another snowstorm just after Christmas brought on a strong east wind. Fine powdery snow accumulated to a depth of nearly nine inches at Winterborne Whitechurch.

It was quite a sunny year and at Wimborne St Giles the duration of sunshine amounted to 1,903 hours.

1909

On the 22nd February sky watchers were rewarded by the appearance of a bluish green meteor at 7pm traversing the sky low down from NE to SW. An observer at Broadwindsor stated that it left behind a luminous track which gradually grew broader and was visible for three hours. At Evershot it was described as being like a streak of electric light. There were frequent clear February skies and by day a remarkable 124 hours of sunshine was registered.

On the 2nd March three inches of snow settled in 48 minutes at Buckhorn Weston then the mercury fell to just 12F. Snow depths at East Lulworth reached nine inches by the 4th March.

There were a number of occasions with over an inch of rain in one day. At Upwey there were no less than seven occurrences. On the 27th July 2.85 inches of rain fell at Winterbourne Steepleton, over two inches was measured in the Cranborne Chase area on 27/28th September with over two inches around Shillingstone on the 21st December.

Although just over the country border at Mere in Wiltshire this picture taken during the severe thunderstorm of May 13th 1906 mirrored the events taking place at nearby Gillingham. An observer there said the storm lasted from 3pm to 10pm and lightning was almost continuous with incessant heavy thunder and hail. By the end of the storm 2.36 inches of rain fell at Gillingham, virtually a month's precipitation.

The High Street, Swanage, on April 25th 1908. The snow was deep enough to built the huge snowman seen in the picture.

Continued deluges during the 18th-21st October 1908 produced over 9 inches of rain on the southern tip of Portland Weymouth saw 5.9 inches. The resultant flooding is shown here in the Park district of Weymouth.

July 1906 was described by many observers throughout England as "a splendid summer month". A good deal of dry weather prevailed with warm days but not excessively hot. It was obviously ideal for the 'Bath Assistant Teachers Association' seen here at Bournemouth enjoying a day on the beach.

Dorset was blanketed with unseasonably late snow 24th-26th April 1908. There was a touch of satire to this photograph taken by 'Sunny' Jim at Sunnyside Cottages, Sunny Road, Bournemouth on the 25th.

Unrest on the weather front

1910

On the 12th May thunderstorms led to some dramatic sky effects in the south of the county. Around 7pm a Broadstone observer remarked "the clouds in the east were of a deep violet-greenish hue, while overhead and in the west-southwest the sky was of a yellow, fiery hue".

At Gillingham there were six successive days with thunderstorms 5th-10th June. The year was remarkable for the number of rainy days. In Upwey rain fell on 220 days. Nearly 50 inches of rain was measured at Broadwindsor and 49 inches at Maiden Newton.

1911

A year remarkable for its summer warmth and drought and the heavy rains of late autumn and early winter. An absolute drought of 28 days from 1st July at Winterbourne Steepleton ended in a thunderstorm and squalls on the 29th. So warm and dry had it been across Dorset a desert-like dust cloud swept ahead of the storm. In Lyme Regis around 4pm a black cloud of remarkable intensity was observed and dust and leaves were carried high into the air. The atmosphere was very close and some eyewitnesses said the clouds rolled in like smoke.

During August the heat and drought returned and at Winterbourne Whitechurch only one day failed to reach 70F. 80F was measured on ten days and 90F or above on four days with a wilting 94.5F on the 12th.

The year as a whole registered 2,137 hours of sunshine in the Poole-Bournemouth area, a record that still stands today.

In December nearly ten inches of rain fell at Beaminster.

1912

A thick fall of snow on the 18th January six inches deep at Chevington Court.

High pressure prevailed during the month of April and it was practically rainless at Swanage, only 0.01 inch [0.2mm] fell.

In a contrast to the hot and dry conditions of the previous August it was cool and remarkably wet with a constant stream of shallow depressions passing by producing 7.5 inches of rain to Beaminster. Overall it was a very wet year with 54.17 inches of rain at Milton Abbas.

1913

At Wimborne St Giles the year's lowest temperature of 20F occurred on 13th April. Some parts had a snow shower on the 12th, the only snow of the 'winter'.

September was a wonderful month with gentle

June 1914 was a very thundery month especially so between the 10th and the 20th. Storms were oftern severe. At Chickerell, a house was struck by during the afternoon of the 14th and a cow was killed in the Parish of Fleet. On the same day a number of people died in London. This picture shows a flock of sheep some 60 in number which succumbed to lightning on the 18th at Blandford.

winds, a soft heat and warm nights, the coldest day registering 58F.

Several waterspouts were seen travelling seaward from Lyme Bay towards Portland between the 6th and 8th October.

1914

A very wet year, nearly 60 inches of rain at Broadwindsor Vicarage. It was the wettest year of a record going back 41 years at Beaminster and here 50.65 inches was measured.

On 11th December commencing about 1am a violent storm ensued from SSW which according to an observer at Lyme Regis reached hurricane force six hours later. Considerable damage was wrought to roofs, chimney pots and buildings generally throughout the district.

It was the two huge armies locked in conflict along the Western Front in this year that led meteorologists who were developing air mass theories to coin the terms "warm and cold fronts". For opposing air masses that clash spawn our changeable weather.

1915

Winter was very mild with temperatures at Winterbourne Whitechurch almost reaching 57F on the 13th January. A bright meteor lit up the night sky as witnessed by an onlooker at Chickerell near Weymouth on the 28th March.

The Christmas holiday was marked by tempestuous weather with torrents of rain limiting people's journeys. On the 27th fierce gales brought down many trees. Dorchester received 11.30 inches of rain during December. Hail lay an inch deep on the 31st.

1916

"As the days grow longer the cold grows stronger" is a well known weather saying and this year it came true. January across Britain was one of the mildest on record. The first ten days gave temperatures of 50F but after the 20th February there was an abrupt change to very cold and snowy conditions. On the 24th February snow covered the county to a depth of nine inches to a foot with ten inches at Cheddington. Snow continued at times in March and on the 27th six inches fell in just three hours at Winterbourne Whitechurch.

It was a wet year with rain on 225 days at Sherborne.

1917

The coldest winter since 1895. Frost occurred daily from 11th January to 15th February with a minimum of 16F. It provided ideal skating conditions and an ox was roasted on the ice bound river Stour at Sturminster Newton. The cold continued into April. At Winterborne Whitechurch eight inches of snow lay on the 11th and the mercury fell below freezing on 15 nights. The mean value for January was 33.5F, February 34.8F and for April just 42F.

June though was warm with temperatures exceeding 90F.

Dorset was on the edge of a remarkable rainfall which affected principally Somerset and Wiltshire on 28th June where in places over 9.5 inches of rain fell, a national record until eclipsed by Dorset's Martinstown in 1955. Even so, 4.4 inches fell at Gillingham.

1918

An early taste of summer in March after quite a mild winter. The mercury rose to 70F on the 24th at Winterbourne Whitechurch yet snow fell heavily and lay on 16th April.

At Whatcombe there were some chilly nights in June. On 11 occasions the mercury plunged below 40F with even a touch of air frost on the 15th for a short time around dawn.

1919

Another mild winter but as can often happen it turned cold in the spring and several inches of snow fell on the 27th April in the Winterborne Clenston area.

An absolute drought of 31 days occurred at Dorchester. It began on 19th May and continued to 18th June and a number of birds perished because of it.

There was a bright display of the Aurora Borealis or northern lights on the 1st October and there was a polar feel to the weather at the end of September with a keen frost down to 27F.

After a wet February, March 1914 brought rain on 27 days in many places and boats were needed on the streets of Swanage.

Droughts, deluges and sun pillars

1920

A mild winter but a cool summer and the 25th May gave the year's highest temperature into the upper seventies Fahrenheit. July was wet beset by frequent depressions and it rained on 28 days at Gussage Manor and a total of 6.3 inches of rain was measured at Beaminster. On 4th July the sky darkened after 1.30pm as an inky black cloud approached from the northwest. An observer in Bournemouth commented "suddenly a violent gale sprang up which bent trees double and rattled the windows followed by a tremendous crash of thunder".

It was particularly cool in August and ice was reported on a pool of water at Sturminster Marshall early on the 20th.

Bournemouth was visited by a curious deluge on 15th October. A nondescript morning with cloudy, grey skies and a little drizzle suddenly became a tremendous downpour around 12.30pm. In just half an hour 1.15 inches of rain fell inundating houses and business premises. Manhole covers were shot into the air at the Central Pleasure Gardens. At Boscombe the tram track was damaged.

1921

The driest year known. Only 13.47 inches recorded at Portland Bill Lighthouse and 14.13 inches at Horton Vicarage. In general annual totals were just 50 to 60 per cent of the long term average.

The year began with a very mild month. January had an average maximum of almost 51F. A temperature of 80F was recorded at many places in each of the months, May to October, with 80F registered as late as the 6th October. Although warm the summer was almost completely devoid of thunderstorms.

A deep low crossed England on the 27th October but in spite of barometer readings as low as 29.46 inches it gave little rain. A severe gale blew for some hours.

By the end of the year the river Stour was lower than anyone could remember. The Reverend Cross's tube well at Sturminster Marshall did not begin to rise until 27th December.

1922

Overall another mild winter with the New Year beginning with temperatures up to 57F on the 2nd but there were frequent fluctuations of temperature as active fronts crossed the county. There was a report of ball lightning at Chickerell on 30th January. The following account is from a Mrs Richardson: "Thomas Isaac [my gardener] was outside the potting-shed at about 7.30 to 7.40am when he saw a ball of fire, apparently about the size of two fists, come out of the clouds and move away in the direction of Chickerell [about NW] till it was lost to view behind the shed, in front of which he was standing. No noise was heard. It was perhaps a meteor, but possibly globular lightning. There was no thunderstorm that day, though there were rather sudden and heavy falls of rain."

On 31st March a depression travelled southeastwards from the Irish Sea to Dover and rain turned to snow giving as much as six to eight inches at Gussage St Michael.

On 6th August 3.72 inches or over ten per cent of the average yearly rainfall was measured at Parkstone as a depression moved northeast across Dorset.

An extraordinary snowfall occurred on 29th October when during the evening it covered the ground in central Dorset and proved to be the only snow of the coming winter.

1923

An extraordinary 9.26 inches of rain fell during February at Beaminster, normally one of the driest times of the year. There was a spell of tropical heat during July with temperatures exceeding 90F culminating in 93F on the 12th. What a contrast at Winterborne Whitechurch, the mercury had fallen to 39F on the 4th July. November was very cold with the mercury below 20F at Winterborne and remained below freezing all day on the 25th.

1924

Striking sun pillars were seen in March. They are caused by reflection of sunlight on cloud consisting of horizontal aligned ice crystals. But sunshine was not often a feature of this year for it was very wet. Rainfall at Beaminster amounted to 14.31 inches above the average totalling a massive 52.71 inches.

1925

Winter thunderstorms are short but can have quite powerful lightning. On the 14th February a cottage was destroyed by lightning at Corfe Castle.

A remarkable June with 313 hours of sunshine in Bournemouth and it was absolutely dry between 29th May and the 2nd of July. Thus June was one of those extraordinary months seldom witnessed in Britain's changeable climate. It was a rainless month. Several other places were completely dry including Wimborne.

1926

The winter was mild save for a cold spell around the 17th January when many places had five inches of snow. Temperatures fell as low as 16F. During February it became almost summerlike with 60F on the 26th.

November was a very disturbed month with a number of depressions passing over Britain. In the Weymouth area rainfall was three times the average and at Winterborne Whitechurch an astonishing 12.24 inches was measured for the month as a whole. Such is the fickle nature of our climate December turned out the driest for over 50 years at Lyme Regis.

There were disturbances of a different sort on the 30th July and 13th August when earthquake shocks were felt in many places. The epicentres were in Jersey and Hereford.

1927

An old weather saying tells us that "April has the face of a monk but claws of a cat" meaning it can prove very fickle as far as temperature is concerned. On the 26th/27th April after warm weather a week earlier the temperature fell to 22F at Bloxworth.

On 11th November there was an early taste of winter with two inches of snow but this was just an outrider to the main event during Christmas evening when rain turned to snow. This heralded the worse blizzard in Dorchester since 1891. Mountainous drifts built up across the Downs and still the snow continued to fall heavily throughout the 26th accompanied by a severe gale. One of the most striking spectacles of this storm were great smokelike clouds of drifting snow streaming from the high cliffs containing St Aldhelm's Head and around Lulworth Cove. Seamen at first mistook it for dense fog.

On Christmas morning conditions at sea were relatively calm and a brightly coloured red-sailed barge glided serenely out of Weymouth Harbour. The Lady Daphne's fortunes were to swiftly change along with the weather. A force nine gale developed off the Devon coast. The captain was hurled overboard and the rest of the crew were eventually rescued by the Lizard lifeboat. The barge was abandoned and the craft finally was cast onto the rocky shores of the Scilly Isles with its sails in ribbons. Mighty storm waves soon pounded it to pieces.

Back on land Bridport, Beaminster and Lyme Regis were completely cut off. Masses of snow nine feet high at Crooked Oak Hill blocked roads from Bridport to Beaminster and there was an even greater depth on the rail line between Powerstock and Toller.

The observer at Dorchester experienced great difficulty in recording the depth of snow owing to the fact that the snow was constantly being blown into huge drifts.

April brought frosts late in the month at Wimborne and cut back sweet chestnut coppice up to a height of 15 feet and subsequent dry weather prevented grow back.

1928

July brought a period of brilliant weather with temperatures soaring above 80F and an absolute drought of 22 days at Melbury House, Evershot after a disappointing June. August was generally fine but a shallow depression deposited just over two inches of rain at Blandford on the 1st.

1929

A year of extremes. It was the coldest winter since 1894/95 and the frost was most rigorous between the 10th and the 17th February when the mercury was continually below freezing falling to 5F at Bloxworth on the 17th. In Weymouth hundreds of bottles of iced milk stood in doorways and the solid surface of Radipole Lake forces the employ of four men to break the ice for the swans. An intrepid youth cycled across it and ice also lined the shore at Weymouth. Abbotsbury it was said rivalled Switzerland as a centre for winter sports with scores of toboggans hurtling down Folly Hill in the snowy conditions.

Perhaps the most extraordinary element of the year's weather was the rainfall. There was an absolute drought of 22 days in March and 28 days in Dorchester during September, the latter being a very warm and sunny month. But more rain fell during November and December than the rest of the year put together. For instance at Maiden Newton 13 inches had been measured January to October whilst in November alone a massive 14.42 inches was recorded. At Lyme Regis November rainfall was three times the average. Springs burst out at Maiden Newton but in spite of all the extreme weather there was a good hay crop, excellent corn crops and mangolds were wonderful according to local farmers.

A fierce gale on the evening and night of the 6th and 7th December was accompanied by frequent flashes of lightning some 100 in three hours at Broadstone.

The 'S.S. Preveza', according to Peter Trim in his booklet 'Shipwrecks from Abbotsbury to Portland', was a Greek vessel bound for Rotterdam. She was refused cargo to Cardiff because she was not insured, and in thick fog went ashore in Chesil Cove on the January 15th 1920 and broke in two. The pictures shows also the grounded Neval tug 'Elida' which has tried to refloat the Preveza. She was finally towed off on the 20th. Thick fog also claimed the admiralty trawler 'James Fennel' when she went onto Tar Rocks on January 16th. She was a total loss but the 16 crew were saved.

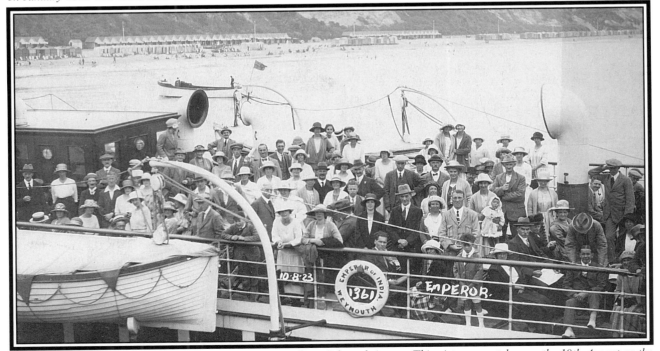

There were some hot spells in the summer of 1923 especially in July and August. This picture was taken on the 10th August as the Emperor of India starts on a cruise from Bournemouth around the Bay with the passengers enjoying fine, warm weather.

The blizzard that began late on Christmas night 1927 and continued over Boxing Day formed huge drifts in lanes and cuttings whilst nearby fields were almost swept bare by gale force winds as here at Bothenhampton.

This group have arrived at Clarence Pier, Weymouth, for the day out in the Summer of 1931. It was not the best of summers with August especially cool and wet but the sun was shining as they posed for the photographer.

Lightning strikes in the Thirties

1930

A very unsettled January especially on the 12th when a violent gale blew across the county, the result of a deep low crossing northern England. The 7.6pm train left Bournemouth Central and ran into a fallen tree. When it finally arrived at Waterloo Station half an hour late it still had a large part of a branch stuck across the engine.

Bus services were diverted three times by fallen trees at Kingston and Poxwell between Swanage and Weymouth. Telephone lines were severed from Weymouth. One hundred trees were toppled at Abbotsbury but perhaps the most dramatic event was the sinking of the 78 ton steamer Forester in Portland Harbour. She dragged her anchor after 7pm on the 12th. Captain Gregory steered at full steam across the harbour to avoid other ships but the steering gear parted and she crashed onto rocks at the end of a breakwater. At least the crew plus one stowaway managed to escape before it sank with all their belongings.

1931

The coldest winter weather occurred during the first half of March when the mercury fell to just 10F at Bournemouth overnight on the 9th/10th. There was also a burst of real cold in October when the mercury fell to 19F during the last week, dry ground helping to lower night temperatures. Only 0.53 inches of rain was measured all month at Shaftesbury, 14 per cent of the average for October.

1932

After a very mild winter March brought very cold easterly winds and the mercury fell to 16F in places on the 13th and this severely delayed the spring with little evidence of leaf and plant growth. Even in the mildest localities there was no sign of the blackthorn blossom. Frost continued into May causing mayhem amongst potato growers.

It turned out to be a very dull year with only 1,445 hours of bright sunshine, the dullest of the century but at least August was quite warm with the mercury above 70F on 24 days reaching 90F on the 19th.

The ingathering of hay was successful and there was a beautiful display of autumn tints finally destroyed by a gale and driving rain on the 30th November.

1933

This was a year of contrasts with a warm and sunny summer but some cold spells. There was extensive frost damage in April when the temperature fell to 20F at Maiden Newton on the 22nd. December too was frosty with temperatures down to 15F.

It was a dry year. Rainfall was eight inches below the average and there developed a serious shortage of water. Winfrith Newburgh recorded its lowest number of rain days, only 116.

On 24th February Dorset was on the edge of a major snowstorm. A blizzard soon turned to rain and 2.53 inches or virtually a month's rain fell at Iwerne Minster with two inches generally.

Temperatures soared to 31C [88F] on the 6th August but as often happens in hot spells thunderstorms broke out. On 13th August two houses were hit by lightning in Fleet Lane, Chickerell tearing a fireplace from the wall. At Wyke Camp lightning struck seven soldiers killing one and badly injuring others.

It was a horrific experience for the soldiers who were crossing a field close to the camp's entrance when a blinding flash of light enveloped Corporal Strong killing him instantly. An eye witness stated that it was as if "a great bucket of red hot cinders had been emptied upon him".

1934

Another warm summer this year especially June and July. At Beaminster the mercury soared to 88F on the 10th July.

December was remarkably mild with scarcely a ground frost and many flowers were still in bloom. Temperatures were more like April. Nationally it was the warmest since records have been derived back to 1659.

Winds blew more or less constantly from the south-west during December, often a wet direction. No surprise that Beaminster hit the headlines for rain with an exceptional monthly total of 13.83 inches, over a third of the yearly rainfall.

1935

A very mild winter but there were one or two bursts of cold in the spring. On the morning of the 11th March four inches of snow lay at Shaftesbury. In May a surge of polar winds brought snow to parts of the county on the 18th and there were sharp frosts. A deep secondary low led to a severe gale on 16/17th September with winds gusting to 80mph. At Swanage there was considerable damage to trees, beach huts and houses. Bournemouth Football Club had its scoreboard completely demolished.

1936

During January over half the days had wind blowing gently from a northerly point resulting in very sunny weather for sheltered Bournemouth. Six days enjoyed over seven hours of sunshine. Conditions on the Undercliff Drive were said to be more like early summer than winter.

In February parts of the county such as at Winterborne Whitechurch experienced heavy freezing rain encrusting grass, hedges, trees and buildings with clear ice. Windows had the appearance of crinkled glass.

It was colder too at Easter with heavy snow showers reported from Winterborne Whitechurch on the 12th April. At Maiden Newton a temperature of only 21F was measured on the 23rd April.

July was cool and wet. At Beaminster the top temperature was only 71F and at Thorncombe nearly nine inches of rain was measured. However August made up for July's failings and was an excellent holiday month. Only 0.08 inches of rain fell at Weymouth and just one day was completely cloudy.

1937

A drenching start to the year. The first three months at Beaminster were the wettest since records began in 1873 with 18.26 inches.

The centre of a shallow depression lay over Dorset on St Swithin's Day, 15th July. Heavy storms developed. From 11am to noon violent rainfall flooded the Park district of Weymouth to a depth of two feet. Holidaymakers had to be rowed to their lodgings for lunch according to the Dorset Daily Echo and Weymouth Dispatch. A total of 3.25 inches fell at Weymouth and 2.95 inches deluged the appropriately named Puddletown. Nevertheless in spite of tradition it turned dry, sunny and warm in August, 83F on the 6th August.

Snow fell again in some quantity during March, a feature of the decade. Nine days had snow.

Later in the year on the 7th and 8th December eight inches of snow caused vehicles to be abandoned at Askers on the Dorchester and Bridport Road and there were reports of snow two feet deep in Shaftesbury. It was in this year that the term "blizzard" was widely used in the press to describe a snow storm.

1938

The northern lights were seen during the evening of the 25th January.

Spring was very dry. At Poole only one inch of rain fell from 1st February to 30th April and in April there was no rain at all. March was one of the warmest on record.

A great gale on 1st June blasted the coast of Dorset. The wind touched 80 miles an hour and as a result miles of hawthorn hedge were blackened and sycamores and planes were turned a hideous yellow clay colour up to five miles inland by the salt-encrusted gale.

Damage was estimated to be £5,000 to trade exhibitors' stands at the Royal Counties Show in Bournemouth. The show continued minus the poultry and rabbit section.

After one of the warmest Novembers on record the run up to Christmas was very cold with sharp frosts and a biting east wind. At Weymouth the mercury did not rise above 28F and over 700 men were laid off at the Portland quarries as water froze in the boilers of steam cranes. Thick snow led to a 'traditional white Christmas'. Drifts six feet deep closed roads in the Coombe Valley. It led to the cancellation of the traditional Boxing Day Cattistock Hunt Meet in Bridport.

1939

There was a somewhat unexpected snowstorm on the 25th January as a deepening low moved along the Channel. It had not been particularly cold but heavy rain turned to snow and in the west and north of the county it reached over a foot in depth. In Cerne Abbas the school bus became marooned on Batcombe Hill and could not be used the following day either so the children from Minterne, Godmanstone and surrounding villages had a day off. Drifts reached six feet on Verne Hill near Lyme Regis. Bournemouth and Boscombe FC became marooned on their way to play Exeter and were forced to spend the night at Bridport.

Overall it was another wet year with a thundery spell in July producing prodigious rainfall totals on the 20th August. At Blandford 4.66 inches or ten per cent of the yearly total fell in six hours and exceeded the total fall from February to June 1938. Yet at Swanage no rain fell.

A shepherd at Hyde Farm, Pimperne near Blandford failed to return home. His body was found around midnight with cuts and burns and it was believed he was killed by lightning as he crossed fields earlier in the evening. In the village there was total confusion as roads and property were flooded to a depth of two feet and in the commotion a dog was run over by a car. It belonged to the shepherd and was probably trying to make its way home.

In Blandford the lower part of the town was under four feet of floodwater.

Wimborne firemen who were called to the residence of Lord Alington, Crichel House, had a harrowing journey. The rain was blinding and roads almost impassable. But worse was to come when they arrived. Whilst pumping away floodwater some of the crew were standing on the lawn next to a flag pole. Moments later a dazzling flash of lightning struck the pole shattering it into myriads of fragments and several officers were thrown senseless to the ground. Amazingly they soon recovered.

(Right) 'The Madeline Tristan' was taking gin from Brittany to Le Harve but was wrecked by a severe gale on September 20th 1930, at Chesil Cove.
(Below) This picture captures a waterspout in Swanage Bay circa 1937. They are simular to tornadoes though not as violent. A funnel lowers from the cloud and a vortex agitates the sea underneath forming a curtain of spray. They often last less than 20 minutes.

Sorting mail by candlelight

SEPTEMBER may be part of the season of "mists and mellow fruitfulness" but the evening of 16th September 1935 proved to be anything but serene when a storm described as being of "almost tropical intensity" roared its way across Dorset with winds in excess of 80mph.

A depression was situated off northwest Scotland and in its circulation was a rapidly deepening secondary low. It hurtled northeast across England and was exceptionally destructive for the time of year.

Structural damage was widespread both on land and at sea. In Poole Harbour around midnight boats were ripped from their moorings and driven on to the promenade. At Sandbanks a craft was even deposited in somebody's garden whilst at Dean Court, Bournemouth Football Club's ground, both the scoreboard and a supporters' hut were completely demolished. Meanwhile on the beach thunderous waves turned 300 beach huts into little more than matchwood.

An extraordinary feature of the destruction wrought on Bournemouth seafront was that within yards of the pulverised beach huts stood sand models of Christ and his disciples, miraculously undamaged.

Inland movement on roads was well nigh impossible as hundreds of trees were blown over. Because they were still in leaf they acted like huge sails and caught the full force of the storm. Wimborne along with Blandford and Shaftesbury were practically cut off for nearly two days.

Telephone links across the county were severely hit with over 400 lines down in the Weymouth and Dorchester areas, 200 in Purbeck and over 1,000 in the Bournemouth district.

Right through the central belt of rural Dorset many dwellings lost roof tiles or thatch and at Wareham two lady holiday makers had to jump for their lives when the houseboat they were renting broke its moorings on the Rover Frome. Postal workers in the sorting office at Wimborne ended up having to sort the mail by candle light after the electricity supply failed, severed by a falling tree.

The storm departed as quickly as it had arrived blowing itself out in the early hours leaving behind a battered and bruised county with much clearing up to do.

(Bottom Left) The severe gale of September 1935 left a trail of wreckage along the coast and many beach huts were reduced to matchwood seen here at Bournemouth.

(Bottom Right) Damaged classrooms at East Howe School, Bournemouth, after the severe gale of September 1935.

The worst flood ever seen

The High Street of Swanage leading to the square and some people queuing for bread were casting an anxious eye on the rising floodwaters in November 1935.

THE autumn of 1935 had been wet and the last thing needed was a vigorous depression crossing Dorset on the 16th. It brought a deluge falling on the already saturated ground. At Steeple in Purbeck 2.58 inches was measured.

As a result a wave of water swept through Corfe six feet deep on the Wareham-Swanage road beneath the castle. Water poured into the rear of homes and out through the front doors. Only the top of a signpost to Studland was visible. The huge volume of water pent up on the hills burst over the road to Wool and Lulworth sweeping away a brick bridge and leaving a chasm in the roadway six feet deep. Tiny rivers became raging torrents with the Sherford stream at Organford inundating a farm, drowning poultry and tearing away haystacks.

In Swanage even the fire station was submerged and the officers had to rescue their own appliances before attending to the many calls for help. In parts of the High Street they pumped out premises at the rate of 15,000 gallons a minute. Water reached the top of a billiard table in the Conservative Club and boats were used to deliver food parcels to those marooned in Eldon Terrace. The force of the water smashed windows as it swept along Kings Road. It was described as the worst flood the town has seen.

A landslide engulfed a milk lorry in 20 tons of muddy earth between Upton and Sturminster Marshall and a small car suffered a similar fate as it rounded a bend and ploughed into the debris. Hundreds of cattle were moved to high ground. The valley below Blandford to Wimborne provided a desolate scene. There were similar sights between Longham and Kinson. One reporter likened it to an inland sea, only the tops of electricity pylons and crowns of trees protruded from the murky waters. In one cottage a lady donned her Wellingtons and walked on the tops of chairs and tables to move around her flooded home.

The Bournemouth Echo estimated that by the 17th November the town had received nearly 10,000,000 tons of rain since the start of month. No wonder there was so much flooding.

Water pouring from The Square over the sea wall by The Parade in Swanage after two and a half inches of rain fell on November 16th 1935

The November 1935 floods in Swanage were the worst the town has seen. Here is another view of the High Street area.

Dorset weather 1940–1949

Weather Window on the Forties

1940

With mean temperatures of around freezing January 1940 was the coldest month for 45 years. The mercury plunged to just 7F at Maiden Newton. Super cooled rain chilled to below freezing fell around the 27th January. On landing it froze instantly into pearls of ice giving pretty but perilous conditions. Cyclists skidded off their machines on Weymouth's Town Bridge. Gentlemen's umbrellas became welded with ice and failed to shut.

May and June were sunny and warm months with the latter producing on average 10 hours of sun a day and 90F was exceeded on four days. The fine weather helped in the evacuation of thousands of British soldiers from the beleaguered beaches of Dunkirk.

August was virtually rainless with only 0.02 of an inch at Creech Grange.

1941

Another chilly January with snow falling on seven days. Poole recorded four absolute droughts [15 days or more without measurable rain] during this year, the longest being 31 days 10th June to 10th July. There was a wet August but the hay and harvest was very favourable.

1942

The third cold winter in a row. The thermometer registered just 9F on 27th February at Wimborne St. Giles another boost for the old adage "as the days grow longer the cold grows stronger". Fog was reported on 13 days in March. At Poole another long absolute drought was recorded this time of 30 days 10th April to 9th May.

On the 2nd August at Trygon [Wareham] 0.74 inch of rain fell in just 15 minutes. This is classified in British Rainfall as a noteworthy fall.

1943

A mild winter, a contrast to the previous three with only three ground frosts at Blandford in January. Spring was early this year and April was a warm month with the mercury topping 70F on four days. The 30th July was a very hot day with 92F in the Chilfrome area.

1944

A dry spring was partly responsible for some large ranges of temperature. For instance on the 26th March around dawn the thermometer read just 29F along the Stour Valley but by early afternoon the temperature rose to 66F.

During May there were frequent frosts with much damage to soft fruit but at the month's end the mercury reached 85F, 89F and 87F on the 28th–30th May.

The fine weather was not to last and it became very unsettled during the first week of June. It led to arguably the most famous of all weather forecasts to be issued, the one that launched Operation Overlord and the D-Day Landings. The thrust of the campaign was postponed from the 5th to the 6th June to make use of a very brief 'Weather Window' to allow the Allied troops to disembark upon Normandy's shores. There was much to thank the Scotsman James Stagg, meteorological adviser to General Eisenhower, for predicting it in such difficult circumstances. Immediately prior to the launch there were 500 shipping movements at Weymouth and between D-Day and the end of the summer 304,000 British and American troops were shipped from Weymouth and Portland as well as 85,000 vehicles. On a sadder note 26,000 dead or wounded troops came back through the port.

1945

A very cold January with temperatures falling unofficially as low as 0F at Wimborne St. Giles and 4F at Tincleton. Many places recorded their lowest ever January temperatures. The most intense cold was preceded by a severe gale and thunderstorm on the 18th. A description in the Dorset Daily Echo stated that at Weymouth one vivid blinding flash of lightning was immediately afterwards followed by a clap of thunder which in the fierce wind sounded like a cannonade fired from hundreds of heavy guns. It was succeeded by a torrential downpour. During the freeze a corporation gardener in Dorchester slipped on the ice and made violent contact with his wheel barrow. He was hospitalized for several days.

February became as mild as January was cold and wild fluctuations of temperature occurred in April bringing some truth to the old expression "don't change a thread till April is dead". On the 17th the mercury rose sharply to a summer like 78F but piercing frosts with temperatures plunging to several degrees below freezing occurred at the month's end.

RADIO PAGE 3

Dorset Daily Echo
AND WEYMOUTH DISPATCH.

FINA

o. 8012   REGISTERED FOR TRANSMISSION ABROAD   THURSDAY, JANUARY 30, 1947   PRICE: ONE PENNY   NEWSAGENTS DELIVERY CHARGE EXTRA

BRITAIN SHIVERS IN GREAT FREEZE-U

Eighth Day Frostbound And Snowbound
Worst Electricity Cuts Ever

THE great freeze-up continues. For the eighth day Britain is frostbound and snowbound, and swept by blizzards.

Temperatures were still below freezing point all over the country early to-day; road traffic was held up and trains were delayed.

All-day electricity cuts—described by an official of the Central Electricity Board as the worst there have ever been—added to the discomfort and difficulty.

THE Southern Railway reported that snow ploughs were out to-day on the Salisbury-Exeter-Plymouth section of the line.

A light engine was stuck in a snow drift between Ashbury and Halwill, near Okehampton (North Devon) and its crew, assisted by railway gangers, dug it out.

In Salisbury and district last night there were 20 degrees of-ground frost and the lowest air temperature was 19 degrees.

Firemen attempting to reach a fire at an army camp on the Plain ran into a snowdrift and had to dig their way through.

With a blizzard raging on Dartmoor, Princetown and district was isolated to-day. The snow is six to ten feet in most places.

"GRIM FUEL TALE"

The big electricity cut started at 7.20 a.m. to-day. It was 25 per cent. in south-west and south-east England, 20 per cent. in mid., east and central, and 10 per cent. in Scotland, north-east and north-west England.

An official of the Central Electricity Board said, "It is a very grim tale this morning. The cuts are the worst there have ever been."

In Scotland, supplies were restored after 40 minutes and the cut in the north-west was reduced to 5 per cent.

FRANCE'S PLIGHT

Shivering France faced gas and other fuel cuts to-day, in addition to restricted food supplies.

The French weather bureau reported that the great freeze-up was likely to last until Sunday. Paris was gripped by the winter's record low temperature of 32 degrees of frost and many people flocked to comparative comfort of underground stations where they spent last night. Cinemas which

Getting Warmer

"It will be very cold, but temperatures will rise somewhat"—official forecast for the period ending at noon to-morrow.

had sufficient black-market coal to turn on the heat were packed.

Coal barges are frozen in canals in northern France. The fishing fleet at Nantes is unable to put to sea.

SHIPPING SUSPENDED

Shipping on the Rhine has had to be suspended.

Ice floes 30 feet high on the River Werra, in Thuringia, have been broken up by dynamite.

As Moscow shivered under a cold snap, spring field work, including preparation for sowing, has begun in southern districts of the Soviet Union, Moscow radio reported.

Weather Forecast

Weather forecast for the 24-hour period from noon to-day:

South-east and South-west England: Moderate or fresh east or north-east wind; cloudy; occasional snow; still very cold, but tempera-

Buckingham Palace Search
Bomb Warning

Officials carried out a search at Buckingham Palace, last night, after a telephone message from a man, who shouted: " Clear Buckingham Palace, because bombs have been placed there to go off on Saturday."

The call was received at Welbeck telephone exchange, just before midnight, and it was traced to a street kiosk.

The message was at once passed on to Scotland Yard, who informed the Palace and special precautions were taken

The search at the Palace disclosed nothing suspicious.

The "Cat's" Whisker

A Streatham family, unable to use their radio because of the electricity cut, listened-in to to-day's 8 o'clock news bulletin with a 1924 crystal (cat's whisker) set.

H.M.S. Vanguard's Protection From Magnetic Mines

Aboard H.M.S. Vanguard, which is to take the Royal Family to South Africa, full precautions will be taken to ensure protection against any magnetic mines not yet swept up, Mr. B. H. Thorp told members of the Engineering Society at Leeds University to-day.

"The Vangard's de-gaussing installation," he said, "comprises six coils of multi-core cable, weighing 30 tons and containing 28 miles of copper-conductor."

The total weight of copper and copper alloys used in the Vanguard was estimated to be about 2,000 tons.

Snow Search For Hurt Climber

A STRETCHER party set out from Fort William, Inverness-shire at daybreak to-day to go to the rescue of a young soldier mountaineer, believed to be lying hurt in the snow on the 3,621-feet peak known as Stob Coire Nam Beith.

Flashes, thought to be signals for help, were seen on the summit last night, and two expert mountaineers, the Rev. R. J. V. Clarke and Mr. William Thomson, set out from Fort William just before midnight to climb the mountain

The climber, who is feared hurt,

ELECTRICITY CUTS A WEYMOUTH MAY B NECESSARY

WEYMOUTH people were warned by loudspeaker to-day that unless they switched off all unnecessary lights and electric fires, power might be cut off altogether. So far the electricity cuts have not affected Weymouth very seriously, said an official, and if the townspeople co-operated there should be no need for drastic measures.

The temperature in the town was slightly higher than yesterday, but there was still 14 degrees of frost. In this morning's blizzard up to five inches of snow fell and road conditions were the worst since 1940, with drifts several feet deep.

One resident was unable to open her doors and had to climb out through a window.

'BUS SERVICES CURTAILED

Many 'bus services were suspended or curtailed. 'Buses have been running to Upwey and Radipole, and as far as Chalbury Corner on the Preston route. It was impossible to resume the service to Wyke and Portland, and the Exeter service was cancelled. A 'bus set out this morning for Bournemouth.

Yesterday 125 men with 12 lorries were out gritting the roads, using 130 tons of grit. In the blizzard at 6 o'clock this morning 130 men went out in 13 lorries. It was hoped to put more lorries on later, and the Southern National 'Bus Company also helped.

TRAINS DELAYED

Mr. F. J. Colls, the Weymouth stationmaster, told the "Echo" that all trains from Bristol, the West of England and London were coming in 40 minutes late, but there were no main line blocks. The 8.2 a.m. autocar service, Weymouth-Maiden Newton, was cancelled.

At Dorchester the major the main roads were passable, but the old borne-road was blocked. children's 'buses run by the Regis and District Motor S all got through safely, from Bere Regis were to reach Dorchester. Ge speaking only a skeleton vice is running to the vill

SNOWPLOUGHS OUT PORTLAND

The situation at Port "terrible," according to veyor, Mr. R. Davison, b negotiated the hill with chains. Snow ploughs work in all parts of the Grit is being spread.

"There are some drifts bottom of the hill," Mr. said, "but those at the far worse."

MAIL VAN DELAYE

A mail van which le chester at 4.45 this morni mails for Bridport, had n heard of again many hour The van's route lay over the most exposed roads in across Askers Down, which drifts had made imp Several vehicles near Askers Road House.

Garage proprietors in have received dozens of help from motorists stran the snowbound highways.

A snow-plough was put on the Dorchester—Bridpo and road gangs were busy ing gravel on the road surf

The road at Stoney He blocked yesterday afternoo a lorry skidded into such tion that other traffic was to pass. Policemen were duty to divert motorists Loders.

(Continued in Back Pa

d-Ocean age Show For yal Family

the battleship H.M.S. Vanguard steams across the tor on the Royal Family's ge to South Africa, the King Queen and the two Princesses be entertained by a full-length y show staged by the ship's any. Arrangements are afoot oadcast the programme to Africa and possibly to Bri-

tatively named "Swing d the Buoy," after the title of pening chorus, the show will be presented ashore at the nard's various ports of call in nion.

arrival in South Africa, a mime extravaganza, "Sinne Sailor" will go into produc-with a view to presentation public in Durban, and Cape to their Majesties on the e home, and to the outlying ishments of Portsmouth hand on return to Britain. tage has been erected by the nard's carpenters aft the er-deck, with full lighting urtain facilities.

rman Transport Faces Collapse"

Hanover railway official d by Leipzig radio, declared nless railways in the British were given back their basic ment (effective locomotives, lass trucks and good coal) would face a "complete col-of the transport system."

ing the war 1,292 miles of y tracks, 1,750 bridges and 0,400 railway engines were yed in the British occupation he said.—Reuter.

F YOUR RHEUMATICS NEVER LET YOU FORGET

take De Witt's Pills

If you cannot work, cannot play and cannot even move about without being tormented by the pain of rheumatism, it is high time you read the following extracts from a letter:—

"I was a very bad sufferer from rheumatism. I decided to give De Witt's Pills a trial. I am now free from pain and I feel wonderfully well."

Mr. W. W.

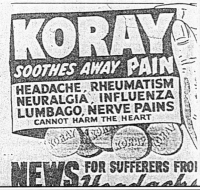

KORAY
SOOTHES AWAY PAIN

HEADACHE, RHEUMATISM NEURALGIA, INFLUENZA LUMBAGO, NERVE PAINS
CANNOT HARM THE HEART

NEWS FOR SUFFERERS FRO

The severe weather of late January 1947, emphasised by the headlines in the Dorset Daily Echo.

1946

A wet year with as much as 55 inches of rain in Minterne, the second wettest total county wide since 1872.

After a chilly first half of March the temperature reached 71F on the 30th and for a few days at the beginning of April. There was a late surge of heat at the end of September when 79F was reported.

1947

A year which turned out to be a meteorological extravaganza full of incident and extremes. Except for the 2nd and 3rd February there was a frost every night 16th January to 11th March. Over England as a whole this February remains the most rigorous since at least the 1650s.

In March Maiden Newton measured a monumental 11 inches of rain and generally it was the wettest March on record.

The summer proved to be very warm and sunny and indeed August was the warmest on record until 1995. August gave a mean maximum temperature of 79.2F at Bournemouth worthy of the Mediterranean and the mercury soared to 92F inland. Generally over Britain the month was the driest known. Even as late as the 6th October the temperature was still up to 75F in the Winterborne Houghton area and the August to November period was the driest on record.

1948

A mild winter though a burst of cold around the 20th February with severe frost and a touch of snow. A week later snow gave way to a mini heatwave, the mercury rising to 61F and by the 9th March peaked at 73F, a record for the time of year.

At the end of a cool July there was a burst of what seemed like tropical heat during the 28th and 29th that took many holidaymakers by surprise. Jumpers were peeled off as temperatures soared to 92F.

At Stalbridge on the 8th August a massive 3.94 inches of rain, more than the monthly average, fell in two hours and was measured by Mr F.B. Harris. This is classified in British Rainfall as being "a very rare fall". It brought a dramatic end to the Bank Holiday and also resulted in the complete abandonment of a Speedway challenge match between the Poole Pirates and Southampton at 30 points all. Torrential rain in Poole quickly flooded the stadium. Scores of campers were washed out at West Bay.

1949

This year was notable for its warmth and dryness. A good year for holiday makers. The average maxiumum at Blandford was 61F a record and the coldest day was only 38F recorded on March 5th. Yet again 90F was reached in July, this time on the 12th.

Pictures from the Bournemouth Daily Echo during the severe winter weather of 1947. Delicate plants succumbed in Bournemouth.

Cold comfort for post-war Dorset

THERE is an old weather adage that runs "as the days grow longer the cold grows stronger" and indeed there is some sense in this as nights are often chilliest in February. The winter of 1947 was to reinforce this belief with the coldest February on record accompanied by protracted heavy snow with deep drifts cutting off many towns and villages. Power cuts and a reduced working week came at a time of austerity following post-war Britain. The winter seemed to last for ever.

For a while in January it looked as if a benign winter was on the cards. Cold east winds had been pushed away by mild westerlies and the temperature touched 50F on the 16th. However high pressure that lay to the south was not content to stay there but moved northeast and by the 21st had taken up residence over Scandinavia. Winds turned easterly and soon the first tentative falls of snow were to whiten the landscape.

On the night of the 28th more substantial snow fell and with a temperature of 15F in Bournemouth and 16F in Weymouth, the lowest recorded in the town since 1900, it was becoming apparent this was no ordinary cold spell. Another snow storm on the 29th brought eight inches to Swanage and over a foot to the Purbeck Hills. By now thousands of men were being laid off as the atrocious conditions curtailed most forms of outdoor work. Shortages of food and fuel added to the depression with shipping halted in the Channel. Road haulage workers stopped working and meat rotted in warehouses. Bacon, eggs, butter, fish and sugar were scarce.

There was to be no let up as a low pressure system off the Lizard brought another six inches of snow on the 30th and snow now lay two feet deep on the road between Blandford and Shaftesbury. Outlying villages such as Porteseham south of Dorchester were unable to receive their delivery of school meals despite 125 men working with 12 lorries and 130 tons of grit in the Weymouth area. Trolley buses could not receive power from frozen overhead lines in Bournemouth.

At this stage of the winter coal and gas were in very short supply and appeals were made by the authorities for householders to cut their consumption to an absolute minimum.

On the 31st hope at last seemed to be in sight with the Dorset Daily Echo carrying news of an impending thaw. Heavy rain fell in the hills and fields were flooded with river levels described as dangerously high. But this proved a false dawn and by the 5th biting, snow laden northeast winds, returned with day time temperatures below freezing even along the coast. To add insult to injury folk had to endure the cold without any electricity. Mr Emmanuel Shinwell, Minister of Fuel and Power, said in the Commons that only industrial establishments engaged in essential work were permitted to use current. Non industrial premises across the county had their power turned off between 9 and 12 noon and 2 to 4pm. Many shops and offices were illuminated by candlelight and even when the power was restored it was at a reduced voltage. Buckingham Palace and Ministry offices operated under similar restrictions. Schools closed so did cinemas and congregations failed to turn up at church.

A further depression moved along the Channel on the 21st and 22nd February bringing yet more snow and temperatures fell to 22F and the cold was made all the more depressing by a singular lack of sunshine with virtually none since the beginning of February. A veritable mountain of snow weighing 15,000 tons had been removed from Bournemouth's streets by mid-month.

Towards the end of the month temperatures did try to rise with 43F in places along the coast. Many people, including the forecasters, thought a thaw was on the way at last. But instead of being washed by mild Atlantic air a depression took a more southerly track and Britain suffered the worst blizzard of the winter. By the 6th March 300 major roads and 15 towns were cut off over England and Wales.

However for Dorset another weapon in winter's armoury was ranged against the county, in American parlance an 'ice storm'. Milder Atlantic air overrode icy air near the surface and nearly three quarters of an inch of rain froze immediately coating everything in a sheet of ice.

Great boughs broke away from trees, ripped off by the sheer weight of the ice. Roads were littered with fallen branches and telegraph wires some of which were coated with ice the thickness of a man's arm. Posts were brought down or were left at crazy angles by the weight measured in tons. All across the southern part of the county anything left in the open was festooned with a shroud of ice.

This was to prove the winter's last fling in the south as subsequent depressions sent warm Atlantic air much further north and there was a rapid thaw causing some of the worst inland floods of the century with the Fenland of eastern England suffering the worst. Indeed March was the wettest of the century with three times the average rainfall.

Over Britain the winter's toll revealed four million sheep lost and 50,000 cattle dead from hunger or cold. 70,000 tons of potatoes and 120,000 acres of winter corn were destroyed by the cold or subsequent flooding and losses were estimated as amounting to £20 million. Some solace did follow, the summer turned out to be one of the best of the century.

Winters along the Dorset Coast are not renowned for their cold. Indeed places such as Swanage and Weymouth are often snow free whilst other areas in Britain are deeply covered. The winter of 1947 was an exception and it was even colder in 1963. This picture shows effect of frozen sea spray at Swanage Pier in January 1963.

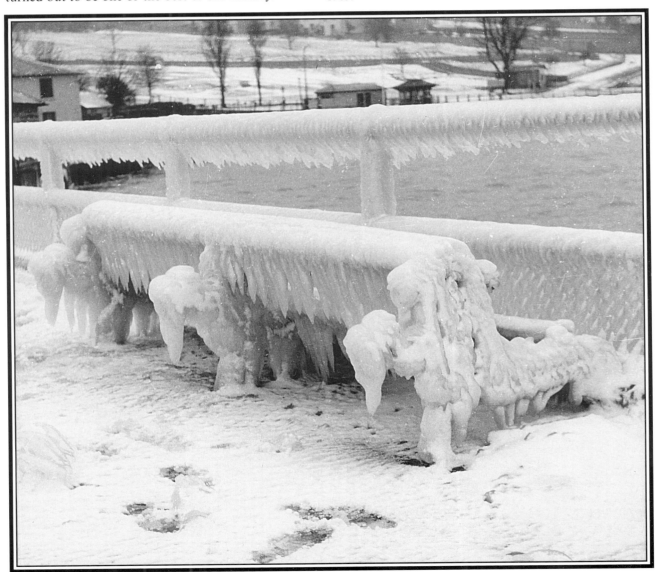

Despite the raging flood waters the milkman still managed to complete his deliveries. July 19th 1955 Upwey.

Roads around Upwey awash after the record breaking rainfall of the 18th July 1955. Upwey itself received a mammoth 9 inches.

Record breaking weather

1950

A heavy snow storm during the early hours of the 26th April affected the northeast of Dorset especially around Shaftesbury as a small depression moved southeast over the country. Up to six inches of heavy clinging snow fell causing much damage to trees, shrubs and plants. One casualty of the icy conditions was a lorry carrying 17 refrigerators which caught fire on the main Bournemouth Road heading south into Dorset from Salisbury.

June was the best of the summer months with 87F reached at Blandford on the 6th.

A gale on the 6th September played havoc with the stands at the Dorchester Agricultural Show.

On the 27th October the maximum stayed below 40F and there was even a touch of snow in parts of the county.

On 14th/15th December a 10 inch fall of powdery snow was measured at Bournemouth.

1951

One of the wettest years recorded, with 56.16 inches at Wynford House and at Weymouth the figure of 40.30 inches was the largest total since the inception of the station in 1883. At Evershot [Melbury House] 12.30 inches of rain drenched the village during November.

It was a noisy year in Sherborne with thunder heard on 18 days. In the early hours of the 27th December fir trees in the cemetery were struck by lightning.

1952

For most of March it was mild but a remarkable blizzard on the 29th led to deep drifts blocking roads and the mercury failed to rise above freezing across the higher parts of the county. A coach load of Weymouth skittle players were trapped by the snow all night but in the early hours five of the party set off to raise the alarm. They walked to Maiden Newton and met the coach driver's son who organized a tow truck. A snow plough was also summoned. It took nine hours before they managed to extricate the vehicle and free the captives.

August will be remembered for the disaster at Lynmouth in Devon where violent thunderstorms led to a tidal wave of destruction through the town. Over 200,000 tons of boulders were swept into the streets

and 34 people lost their lives. From all over Dorset relief funds were set up. Hundreds of pounds were raised in a few days in Weymouth, Bridport and Dorchester from thrift club collections, donations by pensioners and a cheque for seven guineas from the Chesil Beach Holiday Camp.

A Beaminster vicar, Mr McAnally, his wife and two sisters, were caught up in the flood stricken village of Exford high up on the north Devon moors. They were staying at the White Horse Hotel when a six foot wall of water engulfed the building. They all fled to the upstairs rooms whilst down below the refrigerator and kitchen range were floating upside down. Outside the vicar's car disappeared under water. Twenty horses in the stables next door were rescued with just seconds to spare.

Dorset did not entirely escape. Sherborne on the same day, 15th August, experienced a torrential downpour which contributed 3.84 inches of rain or 10 per cent to the yearly total. It inundated the Lady Chapel at the Abbey.

In contrast in Weymouth there was a holiday boom as fine weather returned during the second half of August.

1953

A dry year and Wareham was below par on rainfall by eight inches. The severe gale and resultant storm surge with much loss of life along the North Sea coast overnight 31st January/1st February luckily did not seriously affect Dorset.

It was bitterly cold on the 3rd June at the Coronation of Elizabeth 2nd with temperatures remaining in the low fifties. The month redeemed itself with 83F at Poole on the 29th.

November and December were very mild with day temperatures averaging over 50F during December. Spring flowers were in bloom and birds started to nest.

1954

A classic winter situation with high pressure over Scandinavia and a depression moving southeast along the Channel on 25th January generated very cold east winds and a fall of snow, three inches deep at Poole.

On the 13th May 2.32 inches of rain fell in an hour at Dorchester from 3.15pm. Mr Middleton, the observer at Little Cheam, said that there was six inches of water in his house and that the cattle yard was flooded with the water reaching up to the cow's backs. Disaster was only averted by the collapse of a brick wall.

It was at Charmouth that a funnel cloud was spotted just after 3.30pm on the 8th December and this proved to be the first sighting of a number of tornadoes on this day. A severe one was later to devastate parts of Gunnersbury, Acton, Chiswick and Willesden in London.

1955

In spite of many places in Britain having severe snow-storms during January and February with Operation Snow Drop in northern Scotland, the weather station at Portland Bill reported no days with snow lying.

This year was memorable for Dorset achieving a rather infamous weather record when at Martinstown was measured the British Isle's greatest 24 hour rainfall, a staggering 11 inches on 18th July. This represents six gallons of water a square foot and 170 million gallons on a square mile. This overshadowed a remarkable fall of rain at Blandford, as noted in 'British Rainfall'. On 14th July just over one inch of rain fell in 15 minutes from 4pm. The downrush of rain and hailstones, some over half an inch in diameter, dislodged many slates in the town.

1956

In spite of a very dry Spring water levels remained high and springs maintained their flow due to the previous year's deluges.

February was extremely cold with the mean temperature at Shaftesbury 29.5F and snow lay on the ground for 15 days with air frost on 25 nights. On the 1st February with east winds coming off a bitterly cold Continent the temperature dropped to 14F at Bridport. One motorist stopped for just 10 minutes at Askers Roadhouse and during this brief interval away from the vehicle all his locks had frozen. Other drivers found their breath freezing onto inside windows.

Many children battled to school without a hot meal or warm drink because power supplies had failed due to overloading of the electricity lines. Known as "power shedding" the failure was caused by the exceptional demand brought about by the sub freezing weather. The upper reaches of Weymouth harbour iced over. Wet coal sacks froze together and could not be separated at the Weymouth Co-op Coal Department hindering coal deliveries.

On 29th July gusts of wind reached violent storm 11 at Weymouth as an almost record breaking low pressure system passed northeast over southern England. The pressure fell to 28.82 inches [976mb] in the Stoford-Bradford Abbas area.

There was injury and mayhem in many parts especially to campers on holiday. One child aged sixteen months, asleep in a caravan at Durdle Door, was blissfully unaware of the caravan being constantly buffeted by the gale. The child continued to sleep as the caravan was blown on top of a car. He was dragged out as the caravan righted itself and just before another gust completely wrecked it. Still he slept soundly.

1957

The warmest March on record with many places being completely frost and snow free.

A warm June with the mercury exceeding 80F every day from 12th to the 20th in the Bournemouth-Poole area. Late June was even warmer. Even high up on the hill top at Shaftesbury 88F was recorded. A few heat induced deluges occurred during the month including 2.78 inches at Forde Abbey on the 18th.

1958

Mr James White of the Dorset Natural History and Scientific Society handed over his rainfall recording duties at the age of 92 after 60 years service. At his station at West Street, Abbotsbury, 37 inches of rain fell during the year, five inches above average keeping him busy. His first record published in 1898 was of a dry year with just 23.63 inches of rain.

1959

In a memorable year for warmth and sunshine Bournemouth recorded an impressive 115 hours of bright sunshine in January. By the end of the year Weymouth had measured 2,062 hours of sun. In September only 0.02 of an inch of rain was measured at Portland Bill and it was the driest since 1965 in many parts. Co author Ian Currie was on holiday in the Highlands of Scotland when supplies of water failed at the Guest House where he was staying. Even in October the mercury stood at 75F on the 2nd. As happened in 1911 and 1929 the end of the year turned very wet with 11.05 inches at Beaminster during December.

On the 18th July 1955 this village measured the heaviest 24 hour rainfall anywhere across the british Isles. A staggering 11 inches.

Martinstown storms into the record books

JULY 1955 was for many places in Britain a very pleasant month. In many ways it mirrored the new feeling of hope and prosperity the nation as a whole was experiencing. Apart from the first few days which were cool the month of July advanced like a summer month ought to, dry, sunny and warm. However for west Dorset in particular it would prove unforgettable for quite the opposite reason. Tourists flocking to the Weymouth area in record numbers would soon have something else to write on their postcards to friends and relations. The district was shortly to become a somewhat embarrassed title holder of recording Britain's 'Wettest Day'.

It became very warm from the 11th and even on the coast the mercury exceeded 81F at Swanage and a sweltering 87F at Poole. However humid air over France and Spain edged northwards and thunderstorms over Biscay headed inexorably towards Dorset. Cooler air behind a southward moving front over central England may have augmented the storms and confined them to near the Dorset coast.

The 18th itself dawned cloudy and felt very humid in west Dorset. A few rain drops spattered the ground but the real business did not really start until about 3.30pm with an intensity akin to a tropical cloudburst. Lightning streaked across the sky, thunder crashed. A man from Sutton Poyntz was struck on his way to work during the early evening as the storm obdurately refused to budge from the environs of Weymouth and Dorchester. Two fireplaces were shattered at Bothenhampton as lightning struck a farmhouse. By 8pm at the centre of the deluge over 8 inches of rain or more than 800 tons of water per acre had fallen at a rate of 2 inches per hour. Most of Britain rarely sees such a figure during a whole day let alone in just 60 minutes.

After easing off for a while around 9pm another torrential deluge began slackening after midnight. By this time a record breaking 11 inches of rain measured by Mr N.I. Symons had fallen on the village of Martinstown in the Winterborne valley four miles to the west of Dorchester. An analysis of the storm suggests that an even greater total may have fallen in the area of Winterbourne Abbas just to the northwest but unfortunately no one at the time was recording rainfall in the village. It is estimated that an area of some 200 square miles received over 5 inches of rain. If all this water had been put into gallon watering cans and placed end to end they would have stretched to the moon and back nearly three times, or a staggering three-quarters of a million gallons per square mile.

Unlike the Lynmouth disaster some three years earlier the ground was dry and much of the affected area is chalk downland. The rainfall was absorbed by the porous rock and released gradually as spring water in the following weeks otherwise the effects would have been catastrophic. This is not to say that there was no serious flooding. The Upwey and Broadwey districts suffered major inundations and in the latter an 11-year-old boy was carried off by the raging waters whilst out playing. In spite of this tragedy the casualty rate was fortunately quite low for such an intense rainstorm.

The area around Radipole Lake, Weymouth, fed by the Wey was soon under water during the evening of the storm as the banks were over topped engulfing the Dorchester road in four feet of water and consigning families to upstairs rooms in houses on Marsh Road. Some residents fled their homes and were ferried to higher ground by rowing boat.

Holiday makers had to be put up in local halls as Bowleaze Caravan park was completely awash. The tiny stream running through the site became a raging torrent. Three caravans were swept 200 yards downstream and two bridges were totally destroyed. The rivers Asker and Brid burst their banks and sent three feet of water across the main A35 road cutting off West Bay where the camp site was awash.

In Weymouth local halls were opened up to give shelter to bedraggled holiday makers camping in the area. Over 1,700 telephone lines were out of action around the town.

A wall of water swept down the Wey valley severing the main Dorchester Road [A354] in several places leaving masses of stones and rubble. A landslide blocked the railway line at Maiden Newton for two days. Scouring washed soil away to bare rock and roads had their metalling removed. A hundred soldiers from local depots helped in the clean up operation.

The Chantry, Martinstown, the location of Britain's maximum 24 hour rainfall of 11 inches on July 18th 1955.

REMARKABLE RAINFALL TOTALS FOR 18TH JULY 1955

Location	Amount ins	Amount mm
Martinstown	11.0	279
Friar Waddon	9.5	237.5
Upwey	9.0	225
Elwell	8.31	207
Dorchester	7.5	187.5
Little Cheney	7.32	183
Weymouth	7.15	178.8
Maiden Newton	6.9	172.5
Abbotsbury	6.71	167.5
Sydling St Nicholas	5.75	143.8
Bridport	4.65	116.3

The river Brit overflowing into the harbour at West Bay, July 1955.

Even normally tiny streams became raging torrents and the Bridge Inn was flooded to a few inches of the ground floor ceiling when the normally tranquil river Jordan rose to become a mighty maelstrom.

By the 20th a fund was inaugurated by the Mayor to offer some help to those who had been worst affected by the flooding. Despite national coverage of this immense rainfall Weymouth continued to have a good flow of visitors for the rest of the summer.

Perhaps though it was tempting fate locals thought when at the Regent Cinema the film shown at the beginning of July was called 'Hell and High Water'.

The Caravan Camp Supervisor making his rounds by boat at West Bay during the July Floods, 1955.

Over 700 tons of water per acre fell on Portesham on the 18th July 1955 and the immense run off scoured away this road surface.

Holiday makers at the Bowleaze Caravan Park trying to pull caravans from a normally placid stream but turned into a raging torrent by the exceptional rainfall. Some of the homes were swept 200 yards downstream and two bridges were destroyed.

The ironically named St. Swithins Road, Bridport on the 19 th July 1955. Over England as a whole July was an exceptionally dry month but this was no comfort to people living or on holiday in south Dorset.

So much debris had been washed downstream by the vast amount of floodwater it had to cleared away from the Westham Bridge, Weymouth. The workman are tied onto the parapets as they rake off the masses of reeds, twigs and branches. Taken following following the extraordinary rains of July 18th 1955.

Even high on the hill top at Shaftesbury the temperature reached 88F in late June 1957 and so there was a rush to the beach to cool off and Bournemouth was a popular destination.

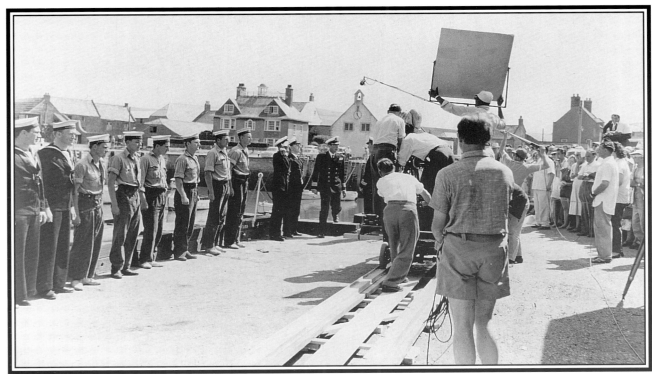

Filming of the 'Navy Lark' at West Bay during the summer of 1959. During this decade there were some very poor summers such as 1954, 1956 and 1958 but 1959 brought glorious weather being mostly dry, warm and sunny from May to October.

There were a number of gales in 1961 and this one provided a rather hazardous environment for the parked Austin on the Preston Road near Weymouth.

Snow lay for 69 days

1960

This was the wettest year in Dorset as a whole since rainfall records were initiated in 1856. At Stock Gaylard 59.79 inches was measured. This however was not the highest individual total as that honour still goes to Cerne Abbas [Melbury] in 1872 with 60.2 inches.

October 1960 was especially wet and on the 22nd the main street of Bridport was under five feet of water. A car left outside the police station was swept 100 yards down the road by the rampant river Birt.

1961

February was unusually mild without a single air frost at many locations yet there were damaging air frosts on the 28th May even near to the coast at Poole.

March was rainless in parts of Dorset such as at Corfe Mullen, Milton Abbas and Branksome.

On 6th October a tornado struck during the late afternoon in Bournemouth lifting most of the roof off a large block of flats called Parade Court on the cliff top. Several nearby hotels were damaged by the flying roof sections and three cars were virtually wrecked. An eye witness spoke of seeing a dark swirling mass approaching from the sea followed by a terrific gust of wind and flashes of lightning and thunder.

1962

The coldest year since 1919. At Swanage the temperature only reached 73F and this on the 3rd September.

The most enduring memory of this year was the start of the great winter 1962/63. During December the sea froze in Poole Harbour and over Christmas Bournemouth was one of the coldest places in the country when the mercury fell to 16F. Snow lay on the last 6 days of the month culminating on the 29th in a classic blizzard of powdery snow as a depression approached the western Channel. Drifts were 12 to 20 feet deep piled up by an east northeast gale. It was the worst snowstorm since 1881 and blocked 200 roads nationally with 95,000 miles snowbound. Farmers in the county threw away 250,000 gallons of milk in just three days because lorries were unable to reach collecting points. Overall 500 farms were unable to get their milk away and the Farmers's Union secretary Mr F. Mitchell said, "The weather's certainly caught us in the pants."

Helicopters were used to drop food supplies and animal fodder to isolated communities.

1963

The winter 1962/63 was the coldest since 1740. The waterfall which drops to the beach at Kimmeridge froze and in Poole Harbour sea gulls were bonded to the ice and long icicles clung to the tail feathers of muscovy ducks at Lyme Regis. Million of dead rag-worms floated out on the ebb tide and festooned the chains of the ferry at Poole.

The snow continued through January and February forcing a battle over food between a famished fox and a badger at Wareham. Snow lay on the ground during the winter for 69 days at Shaftesbury.

1964

Up to this year only 1921 had been drier. The winter period December 1963 to February 1964 was the driest over England and Wales in 250 years of records and estimations. Only 21.83 inches of rain fell at Weymouth.

A few storms did occur and Blandford Church was struck by lightning at the end of May.

There was another cold Christmas with sharp frosts and on the 27th December heavy rain turned to snow giving a six inch cover in the north of the country.

1965

This was the fourth successive colder than average year. At Portland Bill a gust of wind reached 102mph on the 17th January sending 30 foot waves breaking over the rocks. It provided spectacular viewing and the car park by the lighthouse gave the appearance of a summer Sunday it was so crowded.

The old adage "March many weathers" came true this year as it began in deep freeze mode and ended in a heat wave. A vigorous depression moved southeast over western Britain on the 3rd with heavy snow in Dorset up to a foot in depth with huge ten foot drifts. Snow ploughs toiled all night at Tarrant Hinton in the Cranborne Chase area. Three buses were marooned at Winterborne Whitechurch. Shaftesbury was cut off and the Mayor Mr F.W. Sharpe opened the Town Hall as an emergency centre for 50 stranded motorists. Temperatures fell as low as 14F at Hurn and Winfrith. Yet with high pressure over Biscay and moving over southern England during the last week the mercury soared to a balmy 69F.

1966

Shaftesbury had 11 days with snow lying in January and the cold returned with a vengeance mid April when many parts had four inches on the ground with midday temperatures around freezing. Generally it was a wet year. On the 22nd October and 4th November many places were drenched by over two inches of rain with 3.67 inches at Maiden Newton and 3.20 inches at Cattistock, both on the latter date. Many a bonfire was almost impossible to light on Guy Fawkes' Night and at Sherborne even the fire station had to be pumped out as two feet of water engulfed the lower parts of the town. Hundreds of sand bags were requested.

Waterspouts on the 19th October did considerable damage in Poole blowing down chimney stacks, TV aerials, hurling roof tiles to the ground and lifting a hapless moped driver eight feet into the air as he was crossing the Ashley Road railway bridge.

1967

A very wet May and in England the wettest since 1773 and in Dorset the second wettest since 1856. In the Gillingham area it amounted to near six inches. It was wet too in October when Bournemouth recorded over eight inches of rain.

A cold northerly flow on the 7th and 8th led to the development of 'polar lows', small areas of low pressure. A still warm sea and a falling barometer led to a very localised heavy snow fall along the coastal littoral and was the earliest substantial snowfall since 1950. At Long Bredy snow was nine inches deep and traffic was halted. Drifts of five feet closed the Abbotsbury coast road.

Further along the channel coast in Sussex hundreds upon hundreds of vehicles were trapped by deep drifts in the Brighton area. Level snow accumulated to 18 inches.

1968

A cold February though the county missed most of the snow. On the 4th the mercury fell to 17F at Hurn.

There was a very sharp drop in temperature on the 2nd April as a cold front moved south. In just two hours the temperature plunged from 48F to freezing point around Lyme Regis.

This was a year of remarkable falls of rain over many parts of England but the county narrowly missed the worst of them such as in September when the Southeast endured record breaking deluges, some places having over four months rainfall in 36 hours.

1969

The driest October across England and Wales since 1784. The ground was so hard in places that pneumatic drills were being used to break the soil. Less than 0.2 inches of rain fell at Bournemouth. Even as late as the 26th October the mercury reached 70F in Swanage.

Swanage was the sunniest place in the British Isles during June with 304.6 hours of bright sunshine.

Floodwaters holding up traffic on the Wareham to Stoborough Causeway during September 1968. Fortunately the flooding was less serious than that experienced in parts of Southeast England.

Deep snow drifts completely blocked the road to Askerswell at its junction with the A35 in January 1963.

Survivors of the 'Clay Pigeon Cafe' snow siege after being rescued in a joint operation by the army, navy and the police.

Nature paid its debt

FOLLOWING on from one of the warmest and sunniest years of the century, 1960 turned out to be the wettest year in many parts of the county. It was the autumn in particular that Dorset folk still remember as a time of unremitting rain and surging flood waters. The period July to November over England and Wales was the wettest ever recorded back to around 1727.

Low pressure anchored to the southwest sent bands of heavy rain across the county during October. At Poole nearly ten inches of rain fell in the month.

The 23rd of October was especially dramatic. Torrential rain was accompanied by damaging lightning. Residents of Plush in mid-Dorset were left in the dark as the power failed and they could only hear surging water as it rushed into their homes. Furniture and carpets swirled around rooms when the Plush Brook rose five feet. In spite of the rain lightning set fire to a thatched cottage in Affpuddle. Prompt action by firemen could not save the home and it was soon a burnt-out shell. The owners were away at the time.

At Bridport a baby was soundly asleep in her cot when a torrent of muddy water smashed down the front door and burst into the home of a Mr Parker in East Street. He immediately thought of his young child asleep in an adjoining room. He rushed in and was just in time to see the baby's cot float out of the house and along the street. He dashed into the road and retrieved the cot with baby still soundly asleep inside. In another part of the street a 250 gallon paraffin tank at the Askers Filling Station was torn from its pedestal and carried 50 feet to wedge against garage doors.

At another property a lady was nearly swept off her feet when the French windows burst open and water poured into her home.

One pregnant woman needed medical attention when her car was caught in a wave of water. She was helped to a nearby house and a doctor was called and arrived by boat.

At Bridport and District Laundry the whole place, office, works and boiler house, was inundated by the worst floods known by the staff. The railway line between Bridport and Maiden Newton came to a halt when flooding undermined the track.

Beaminster was hit by over one and half inches of rain in just two hours causing mayhem. Police Sergeant Harold Dore left his car outside the station in the Square only for it to be swept 100 yards away by the rampaging River Brit. Another car was badly damaged when it was swept down Prout Bridge Hill. One man had to make a five mile detour just to go 200 yards as he could not cross the Square. The Beaminster Dramatic Society suffered damage to their stage scenery for a play 'House by the Lake' but worse still was the damage at Beaminster Milk Factory where eight tons of milk powder was afloat and several tons of cattle powder submerged. If this was not enough the factory's electrical equipment became clogged with mud.

There was some joy too. The boys of Beaminster School were given a couple of days off to allow flood water to drain away from their classrooms. Surprisingly two bee hives which had been swept away were found, one caught in a wire fence and the other wedged in a hedge and happily the bees were still flying busily in and out.

Elsewhere across the county at Powerstock a car and a garage owned by a Mr Percy Gale was pulverised and huge chicken sheds swept over hedges with great losses to livestock. At Hooke the main street was turned into a river 40 feet wide flooding many homes and at Netherbury a boat was launched to rescue a stranded motorist. In Bradpole a heavy mahogany counter was floating around inside the village shop and Post Office and in Puddletown even the ducks had to be evacuated as their hut was flooded.

Flood appeals were launched in Bridport and Beaminster where free coal was delivered. The appeals raised over £1,200 in just over a week or so with donations coming in from as far away as London. Emergency feeding and clothing centres were set up and Flood Wardens were appointed in Bridport to coordinate people who possessed telephones. They were urged to register with the police in order to warn residents in the vicinity.

There was also a flood of a different kind as local book shops were inundated by orders for the book Lady Chatterley's Lover. The famous court case concerning this controversial volume concluded in favour of publishing it.

The inside of Mr Barret's house in Beaminster reveals the dreadful extent of the October 1960 floods. The muddy waters reached chest high as seen by the scum mark half way up the door frame.

Almost Siberia

The winter of 1962/63 was the coldest since 1740 and even places along the coast suffered icy winds. Sea spray froze instantly onto the superstructure of Swanage pier in January 1963.

A S THE inhabitants of Dorset enjoyed their Christmas revelries on Boxing Day 1962 few would have guessed that they were about to experience the coldest winter for over 200 years.

The weather had been bitter for several days with sharp frosts as low as 16F at Poole early on Boxing Day but a weak front was moving southeast over Britain. Would it bring milder weather? At first during the evening it brought freezing rain. One Bournemouth resident recalled "the roads were like skating rinks and that was before the real fun and games began". However just after 1am on the 27th the first flakes began to fall, the vanguard of the Siberian conditions that would lay siege to the county for over eight weeks. By dawn Dorset was covered in a white mantle up to six inches deep.

Quite often along the south coast it warms up after a fall of snow but not this time. The thermometer remained stubbornly below freezing and more snow fell. Major problems were caused for road traffic and many remote villages were virtually isolated from the outside world. On the Wareham to Weymouth road [A352] police had to spend three hours digging out a stranded petrol tanker which had completely blocked the crossroads at Wareham. At Christchurch the West Hants Water Co had to use steam jets to break thick ice on the River Avon in order to draw off the 15,000 gallons of water needed to keep their customers supplied. Meanwhile snowploughs fought a desperate battle to clear the runways at Hurn Airport.

Although this heavy fall of snow was troublesome it was merely the opening shot to a far more vicious assault. Waiting in the wings off southwest England was a deepening area of low pressure armed with a fearsome mixture of fine, crystalline snow and gale force east winds and it had Dorset in its sights. Early in the evening of the 29th December it struck engulfing town and country alike. Huge drifts formed almost instantaneously, visibility dropped to a few yards, garden walls and country hedges disappeared and roads became unrecognisable and impassable.

A family of five were entombed in their car on Osmington Hill near Weymouth and by the time help arrived the following morning the two eldest occupants of the vehicle had perished and the three remaining travellers were suffering from severe hypothermia. On the Dorchester to Yeovil Road things were just as bleak. A coach party had to battle through the worst of the blizzard after their coach became stranded. They fought their way to the near-

by Clay Pigeon Restaurant where they were cared for by the owner and his wife until they were rescued in a joint operation by the army, navy helicopters and the police, conditions were so bad.

Whilst the weary travellers were finding deliverance at the Clay Pigeon another coach was marooned at Crichel Down on the main Blandford to Salisbury Road. Mr Mick Ware, landlord of the Crown Inn at Tarrant Hinton, borrowed a tractor and horse box in order to liberate the passengers from the vehicle which was by now almost buried. Mr Ware recalled that the blizzard was so fierce that when he stepped out of the horse box he could hardly breathe as the air was filled with myriads of whirling icy granules. Showing considerable courage he and his loyal farm worker 'Dusty Miller' made two trips to take passengers back to the Crown Inn where they were given hot soup by Mrs Ware and then bedded down in the bar for the rest of the night.

The blizzard seemed to be engulfing everything in

Roasting an ox upon the river Stour at Sturminster Newton during January 1963.

its path. At Compton Abbas two double-decker Hants and Dorset buses were buried up to their roof tops. Tens of thousands of gallons of milk had to be thrown away as lorries were unable to reach collecting points.

Finally the winds subsided and the snow ceased. The big clear up operation began. In Bournemouth alone 450 men using 60 diggers, 77 lorries and 1,500 tons of grit battled against the elements. Away from the main centres of population major and minor roads alike would remain impassable for at least a week. All over the county RAF and Navy helicopters flew dozens of missions dropping much needed food supplies and lifting out the sick and injured.

Surely the weather would abate now? However as January drew on the cold intensified falling to just 7F at Winfrith on the 13th and during the fourth week dense freezing fog shrouded the countryside. Seagulls froze to the ice in Poole Harbour and there were reports of starving foxes battling with badgers over scraps of food.

As February arrived this cruel winter was not yet ready to release its grip and snow once again returned adding a few more inches to that which had lain throughout January. This was by now the longest spell of intense cold Dorset had endured in the twentieth century. Nevertheless, mid-month temperatures rose a little above freezing by day, just enough to start a thaw and hundreds of acres of farmland in north Dorset were now under water, but winter returned with more fresh snow on the 21st.

A measure of how cold December to February had been was felt at Shaftesbury, high on the Dorset hills, where the mercury averaged 2F below freezing during these three months and snow covered the ground on 69 days.

Fortunately as February gave way to March sunshine and slowly rising temperatures led to a gentle thaw and there was no repeat of the disastrous flooding experienced at the end of the previous great winter of 1947. Dorset slowly became verdant again.

A bus making its way through 'mountains' of snow at Richmond Hill, Bournemouth, in January 1963.

A scorching summer and a savage snowstorm

1970

The effect of altitude and proximity to the coast considerably alters the amount of snow cover a locality receives. At Shaftesbury nearly 700 feet above sea level and well inland there were 16 days with snow lying during the year but at Weymouth snow cover was nil. Christmas here was not white but deep drifts blocked the road between Bridport and Dorchester and generally away from the coast there was a cover of snow.

Annual rainfall was virtually average but November brought rain on every day somewhere in the county, Winfrith recording 8.65 inches.

1971

A mild winter but the summer was cool especially June and August. At Beaminster June was the wettest since the commencement of the record in 1900 and many places received nearly 6.5 inches of rain. The 9th July brought thunderstorms accompanied by violent rain. Sturminster Newton measured 1.72 inches in just two hours.

An excellent halo display was seen on 20th July at Charminster.

1972

Winter finally arrived at the end of January with some very low temperatures in an easterly airstream. The mercury fell to 14F. Snow was not forecast and gritting teams were stood down, but a surprise three inches fell and when grit was applied it was too cold for it to work and the resultant chaos on the roads was more than the modest fall justified. A mile of stationary traffic was snow bound in Ferndown.

The icy conditions did not deter one house purchaser who queued all night at Poole outside a site office where 16 homes were being offered for £6,695. By 9am seven other people had joined the line.

Many places had failed to reach 70F by the end of June with some days bringing temperatures in the low fifties Fahrenheit. This was possibly caused by an excess of sea ice off Newfoundland.

It was a wet year at Minterne with 53.92 inches of rain, the most anywhere since 1960. At Dorchester the period January to the end of May gave 23.5 inches of rain, the highest total so far this century. The rainfall exceeded 150 per cent of the average in each of these months.

An inch of snow lay around Dorchester on the 17th November.

1973

A very dry year, less rain than in 1964 with only 19.48 inches at Abbotsbury.

On the 26th July a whirlwind some 40 feet in diameter caused panic among holiday makers as it passed over the beach at Canford Cliffs, Poole.

1974

An unusually high Spring tide unfortunately coincided with gale force winds producing serious flooding at West Bay during the 9th to 11th February. Five feet of water flooded the premises of Woolaway Construction Ltd in West Bay Road causing thousands of pounds worth of damage. The Post Office located on an island in the middle of the River Brit was completely marooned and two feet of floodwater covered the floor damaging refrigerators.

A big clear up operation was mounted to remove hundreds of tons of shingle made worse by encrustation of tar washed ashore.

Areas surrounding Weymouth Harbour were swamped with water streaming into houses in Cove Street.

A graphic description of an encounter with a waterspout off Portland on 31st August 1974 was revealed in the March 1976 Weather Magazine. Mr B. Kenyon a yachtsman from Winchester wrote, "Between 0400 and 0500 on Saturday morning we were some four to five miles off Portland, the weather had closed in ... the sea was very lumpy and uncomfortable and it had started to rain ... Very heavy clouds appeared all round. About this time severe electric storms could be seen over Portland and Weymouth. We decided to make for Weymouth. Electric storms became even more severe and the wind a little stronger. About this time a column, Admiralty grey in colour, was seen to starboard of us. It dawned on us that it was the same shape as the whirlwind in The Wizard of Oz. We dropped the foresail and secured it to the safety rails as quickly as we could and lashed ourselves with the spare sheets into the cockpit ... The spout increased in size [or came nearer]. We were eventually able to see the shape and formation and it appeared to be anticyclonic, water turbulent at its base. The water could be seen rising into the column, the colour at the base was a muddy green-brown, though as you looked up the column it became more blue-grey ... it was between 250 and 300 yards away passing us down the starboard side and astern. At the same time an extremely severe electric storm was lying around the boat and forked lightning was quite frightening, appearing to be a yard or so in width. We kept our hands away from all metal parts, said nothing to each other but were rather shaken."

The year as a whole was the wettest since 1960 and an almost unique occurrence took place as far as temperature was concerned. At Dorchester and many other places October was colder than December, the latter being the mildest since 1934 and devoid of any air frosts. October itself was the coldest in the Bournemouth record.

1975

A mild winter but a cold spring with the mercury falling to 21F at Winfrith on the 6th April and throughout southern England there was great damage to orchards which had blossomed early. The pear was particularly badly affected.

Parts of Britain saw snow falling on the 2nd June and one county cricket match was abandoned without a ball being bowled in Buxton, Derbyshire, due to a thick mantle of snow, but in Dorset the weather story was a June totally rainless at Poole.

The summer turned out very warm, especially so in August which was the warmest since 1947 and the second warmest for 300 years.

Bournemouth was the sunniest locality on the mainland of Britain with nearly 1,959 hours of sunshine.

1976

This year will long be remembered for the hot summer and lengthy spells of drought. On the 28th June the mercury soared to 93F at Winfrith and in the Bournemouth area a remarkable seven consecutive days with over 90F, 26th June-2nd July is without parallel. By the end of June rainfall totals were less than 45 per cent of the average and the month was the driest since 1896 at Dorchester with just 0.08 inches of rain. On 30th June a humidity reading of a mere 18 per cent was measured at Weymouth.

There were many heathland fires and on the Dorset-Hampshire border near Ringwood elderly patients were wheeled to safety from St Leonards Hospital as wind-fanned flames leapt ever closer to the buildings.

There was great concern over the little bird the Dartford Warbler, as many acres of their habitat had been destroyed by the fires on the parched heathlands. Tankers delivered water to Shaftesbury during a 38 day absolute drought spanning June and July.

1977

Most of Britain experienced a dry July but in Dorset a violent storm centred more or less in the same place as the 1955 record-breaking rains brought almost four inches to Friar Waddon during the early morning of the 12th. Most of this fell in only a few hours.

On the 8th August there was a report of a curious fall of grass and some soil from the base of a shower cloud over the Poole area.

1978

An exceptional blizzard during the weekend of 18th and 19th February was arguably the worst since January 1881. Dorset was virtually cut off from the outside world and helicopters from Portland flew dozens of missions.

Heavy rain fell at Winfrith on the 31st July with nearly three inches in 13 hours.

The autumn was for the most part warm and dry with temperatures reaching just over 74F at Poole on the 12th October and as late as the 8th November the mercury topped 65F. Over England and Wales there have been only four drier Octobers since 1727. Much of Dorset had less than 0.2 inches of rain. Across England it was the driest autumn since 1752.

December certainly redressed the balance with a very disturbed spell of weather around the 11th to the 13th as a deep low lay to the west of Ireland with air pressure down to 28.00 inches [948 millibars]. Winds gusted to over 80mph and for two nights running Portland was completely cut off from the mainland by mountainous seas which led to the collapse of the causeway. Hundreds of people had to be evacuated from their homes in the early hours. Water gushed over the Chesil Bank. The wind also blew the roof off the Portcrete Stone Factory blocking the road below.

On the penultimate day of the year below freezing air spread in from the Continent but just to the south over Brittany it was very mild with temperatures in the 'fifties'. A frontal system separated the two air masses and an area of low pressure developed and ran along the Channel producing a snow storm over southern England during the evening. It caught many people unawares, including over 200 teenagers attending a discotheque in Bournemouth. All routes out of town were blocked and they were forced to stay the night trudging home on foot the next day. The roads were still chaotic in spite of the application of 600 tons of salt.

The icy weather on New Year's Eve caused 180 casualties, mostly fractures, at Poole Hospital as temperatures fell to 12F.

1979

January and February together were the coldest since 1963. Unofficially the mercury plummeted to just above 0F at Beaminster. The first May snow to lie since 1955 fell at Dorchester and was two inches deep.

A small depression moved north from Biscay on the 30th May. Torrential rain caused widespread flooding exacerbated by weeks of wet weather. At Wetherbury 2.55 inches was measured. Poxwell, Winfrith, East Knighton and Symondsbury were three feet deep in water. A wall of water swept through Charmouth and dozens of caravans were

tossed like matchboxes into the flood. For one Surrey family it was a nightmarish experience. Their caravan was sited near to the river Char at the Dolphin Holiday Camp, when it was engulfed by the swollen stream. The four children, two adults and a dog, scrambled on to the roof and thence into a tree, clinging to its branches for two hours. Rescue involved a helicopter securing lines to the tree, and a boat from the Lyme Regis Adventure Centre being winched across the foaming river. Meanwhile at Hengistbury Head, Bournemouth, a land slip partly buried a group of girl guides and they had to be dug out of the debris.

On the 15th December a gust of 90mph was measured at Portland and a slow moving frontal system gave 3.55 inches of rain at Evershot on the 27th with widespread flooding. The month had begun in extremely mild fashion with the mercury reaching a spring like 62.6F on the 5th near Kington Magna.

East Beach at West Bay in February 1974. An unusually high Spring tide and a gale force wind led to serious flooding.

Fran Lockyer, the Weather Observer at the Old Higher Lighthouse Portland Bill, took this dramatic picture of a water spout at 08.30 hours on September 12th 1993. At one point there were two spouts. With an estimated diameter of 200 feet it came to within half a mile of the shore and then headed northwest across Lyme Bay.

Floodwater on the streets of Blandford in late December 1979 meant Police had to swap the patrol car for a rowing boat.

The evacuation of an elderly resident from his flooded home in Leigh Road, Wimborne, late December 1979.

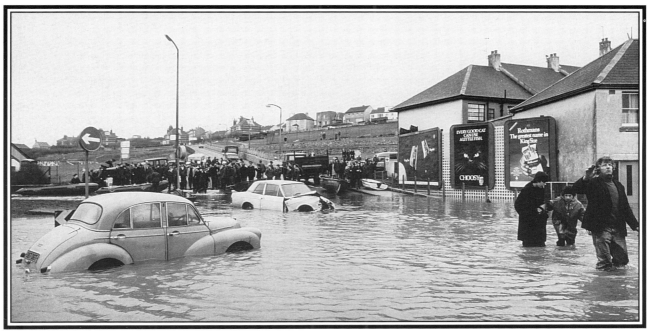

Both in December 1978 and February 1979 there was terrible flooding to the lower ground at Chiswell below the Isle of Portland. On the latter occasion it was a remarkable combination of conditions that led to storm waves, generated thousands of miles away in the Atlantic, to reach Portland. They swept right over the Chesil Bank. These four pictures show the pounding Chiswell took during this winter. Beach Motors in the top picture has since moved to higher ground.

The dramatic rescue taking place at the Dolphin Holiday Camp Charmouth on the 30th May 1979 when caravans were swept away by a wall of water following torrential rain.

An almost submerged car on the Loders to Uploders road 30th May 1979. The equivalent of nearly a month's rain fell on this day following weeks of wet weather.

The blazing summer

Huge fires broke out during the long hot summer of '76. This aerial shot at West Moors illustrates the sheer scale of the blazes facing the firemen.

THE year of 1976 still boats the most talked about summer amongst Dorset folk. It was the summer of parched fields, burning sun, blazing heaths and woodlands, when many of the county's rivers were little more than trickles. Indeed some disappeared completely.

Day after day of hot sunshine from a clear blue sky is nothing short of a miracle for the holiday-maker but a living hell for farmers and especially the fire-fighter.

The Great Drought of '76 was not just about a long hot summer. It was the cumulation of a prolonged period of meagre rainfall. The total for January through to the end of August brought a tiny 7.3 inches, the lowest figure in a record back 140 years. Rainfall had been below average since December 1974.

There was a taste of things to come in early May when a short heat wave led to 82F being measured in many parts. The real heat began on the 22nd June and for 14 consecutive days the temperature topped 90F somewhere in southern England. At Hurn Airport it soared above 90F for seven successive days, reaching 93F on the 27th June, a station record.

The longest run of days with no measurable rain was 45 at Milton Abbas in July/August, which came on top of three other periods of absolute drought, including 17 days in April, 22 days spanning May/June and 19 days June/July.

The drought and great heat wave combined to provide the ideal conditions for the propagation of heath and forest fires and some proved devastating. As the summer wore on the situation became ever more dangerous. Early in July 150 acres of countryside was destroyed in a blaze at Blackdown Forest near Hardy's Monument. Fire crews had to ferry water in bowsers from Portesham village pond two miles away.

In the east of the county August saw fires breaking out on a daily basis. Some were extinguished only to start again the next day having smouldered underground through the peat soils. One fire at Horton Common was started when a whirlwind picked up embers from one burnt area only to deposit them on another part of the bone dry common, starting a conflagration a mile wide. Another inferno destroyed 50,000 trees in Hurn Forest.

Meanwhile at St Ives near Ferndown 250 acres of woodland was decimated when a 50 foot high wall of flame moved at 40mph across the area lead to the evacuation of 350 patients from a nearby hospital. Many were in beds and wheel chairs and they thankfully emerged unharmed through a pall of black smoke, saved by a last minute change of wind direction. The main A31 road was closed and hundreds more people were moved from nearby caravan sites. At one point a military fuel dump near West Moors was almost encircled by flames. Altogether 250 firemen and 110 soldiers using 37 fire appliances and two 6,000 gallon milk tankers commandeered from the Milk Marketing Board fought to control the blaze.

Over 500 people were trapped in Matchams Stadium near Christchurch whilst fire raged all around them. Luckily the stadium was not set alight and the relieved spectators left by a service road which was charred on either side.

On a lighter note, Sparky a pony from Chalbury near Wimborne, got decidedly thirsty in the hot weather and went looking for water. Unfortunately he found a swimming pool belonging to a Mr Roger Holman and promptly fell in. It took 11 firemen and several volunteers four hours to hoist him out.

At Fleets Bridge near Poole motorists were amazed to find three feet of water on the road. A 24 inch water main had burst, flooding the road and surrounding gardens. All this at a time when Wessex Water Authority were considering bringing water by train from Scotland.

As August drew to an end it seemed as if the drought would continue on into the autumn, a situation that would have dire consequences. Already Denis Howell had been appointed Minister of Drought to coordinate operations. but just as many people were about to lose hope of ever seeing rain again, the wonderful British climate came to the rescue. Starting with impeccable timing during the August Bank Holiday, 15.5 inches of rain fell on the county over the next two months. Indeed by the end of the year the rainfall total was only five per cent below normal. The drought was simply washed away.

Here at West Moors livestock are being evacuated from the path of huge infernos raging across the surrounding heathland.

Many ponds dried out during the Summer of 1976 including this one at Worth Matravers in Purbeck. Rivers such as the Stour became mere trickles and some disappeared completely.

The blizzard of February 1978 was comparable to the infamous January 1881 and March 1891 events. This picture shows the van belonging to Mr Thompson an organ builder engulfed by a drift in North Square, Dorchester.

White out

FEBRUARY 1978 has remained in the memories of many Dorset folk. The county endured the rigors of a brutal snowstorm that brought isolation and disruption on an almost unprecedented scale save for the monumental blizzard of January 1881.

The month began meekly enough with an unusual mix of rain and westerly winds. However by the 9th a strong easterly airstream had become established bringing sub-freezing temperatures and snow showers. Temperatures fell to 21F at Bournemouth, the coldest conditions since 1972 and by the 15th the mercury had fallen several more notches to 18.5F.

Mild air is never far from Britain's shores in winter and an area of low pressure looked as though it would warm things up as it approached the southwest. It moved across Devon and Cornwall and tracked southeast bringing moist air to Dorset and turned sleet to heavy snow maintaining the cold easterly flow. Main roads around Dorchester, Blandford and Shaftesbury were blocked by up to five inches of snow. Further east firemen had to cut free a couple from their car which had left the A338 Ringwood to Salisbury Road and hit a tree in the appalling conditions. The following night another area of low pressure slipped southeast over the West Country leading to a repeat performance. The snow fall that ensued was the worst across Dorset since the Arctic winter of 1963, with six inches of snow falling in many parts, especially the north and west of the county. The main A35 road was blocked at Yellowham Hill near Puddletown by a string of jack-knifed lorries and there were severe delays at Bere Regis and at the Baker's Arms roundabout between Poole and Wareham. To the west of Dorchester most roads were impassable for a time. The Bournemouth area only saw a two inch fall but it would not be long before it would feel the full force of a record breaking snowstorm.

Saturday 18th dawned cloudy and cold with a biting easterly wind. By lunchtime a southeasterly gale was screaming across the county and with temperatures around freezing point the chill factor was severe. In towns across Dorset streets were deserted as people tried to stay out of the cold. On the coast huge waves pummelled east facing beaches and promenades. Diners in the sea front Mowlem Restaurant at Swanage, were treated to an awesome display as waves crashed against the base of the building. The sea undermined the huge stone and concrete face of the sea-front wall at West Bay, Bridport, breached the esplanade road, damaged a row of brick chalets and caused considerable flooding. Late in the afternoon the first crystalline flakes appeared blowing in the wind and snaking like loose sand across the roads made dry by the unrelenting gale.

Mid evening saw a full scale howling blizzard right across the county and as midnight approached the severity of the tempest made Dorset folk realise that this was no ordinary snowfall but by then many unknowingly had become prisoners in their own homes. Even in Bournemouth 150 teenagers were forced to settle down for the night at the Town Hall after attending a disco, because all roads out of the town had become impassable. Near Blandford a family returning from London to their home at Lady Baily Caravan Park had to spend the night trapped in their car. Luckily they had a little food with them and managed to hold out until morning when they were rescued by the police and farm workers who took them into Blandford to find accommodation.

Throughout the night the blizzard raged and by first light on the 19th huge drifts up to 18 feet in height had buried Dorset. Great swathes of snow had made roads indistinguishable from the adjacent fields and hedges. Some rural cottages were accessible only by upstairs windows. The north and west of the county were literally buried and completely cut off from the outside world. In the more remote villages such as Worth Matravers in the Purbecks it would be another five days before travel was possible again.

The snow was not the only culprit in causing mayhem. The severe easterly gale with a mean speed of 58mph at Portland during the evening of the 18th had brought down many power lines blacking out large areas. Some villages would remain 'in the dark' for over 36 hours. Pumping stations failed as well, cutting off water supplies. Telephone lines were brought crashing down. Meanwhile the snow continued unabated throughout the 19th.

Early on Monday 20th the snow finally ceased, but Dorset, along with much of southwestern England, was at a standstill. The only way out of the county was along the A31 to the east of Bournemouth, heading into Hampshire, which had not quite felt the full force of the elements but none the less still suffered much disruption.

To the west of Bournemouth every road was blocked or had been closed by the police so as to initiate rescue and ploughing operations.

At Fontmell Magna near Shaftesbury a bus had been completely buried. Helicopters were now being used to help ferry supplies to outlying areas and provide hospitals with blood. They even provided chicken feed to one farm burdened with 100,000 starving birds. In Purbeck an ambulance was towed across fields, by a tractor, to Morden, whilst an armoured vehicle from Bovington Camp battled its way through to Bere Regis to collect a doctor to treat a lady who had collapsed in her home. The patient was taken to Poole Hospital where she sadly passed away later in the week.

An 18-year-old mother-to-be, in labour, was being taken to hospital by ambulance when the vehicle became stuck in a snow drift. The journey from Bridport to Dorchester hospital should have taken around 30 minutes. Mrs Lee gave birth within the confines of the vehicle, ably assisted by the ambulance man Jim Williams and eventually the now two passengers made it to the hospital after the ambulance was pulled out of the snow by a police Land Rover.

All Hants. and Dorset bus services were cancelled and refuse collections were a non starter. The County Council used over 150 snow clearing devices but despite heroic efforts, by Tuesday 21st only two main roads west of Bournemouth were passable, the A35 to Dorchester and the A351 to beyond Wareham. Purbeck was still out of bounds to anyone except the police and essential rescue services.

The well-known singing group the Yetis were among those stranded as well as 11 families re-living the Iron Age for a BBC TV film in a secret encampment somewhere near Shaftesbury. They snuggled up in rough wool and fur and coped well with the Arctic conditions.

On the railways things were a little better and the main line link with Weymouth had been reestablished. The first train through carried loaves and milk for the outlying rural areas. A measure of just how severe the blizzard had been was gained when the supply train reached Upwey. Its doors could not be opened because the depth of snow on the platform was greater than the height of the train.

The storm generated enormous cost to the farming community. Hundreds upon hundreds of sheep and lambs were buried in the huge drifts and lambs born out in the snow simply died of exposure. Dairy farmers poured milk away or gave it to locals because tanker drivers were unable to reach most farms. An estimated 1.5 million gallons a day were lost.

Some four days afterwards many people who had been visiting the county or trying to return home were still trapped at inns and hotels. Indeed many outlying villages would remain unapproachable until the following weekend.

The clear-up operation would run into hundreds of thousands of pounds. The damage at West Bay alone was assessed as £600,000. Estimates for the blizzard throughout the southwest was between £5 million and £10 million. Damage to trees was considerable in parks and gardens. Roads needed repair. The government's weather minister, Dennis Howell MP, was appointed to manage the recovery and promised that 75 per cent of emergency spending plus all airlifting operations would be met.

Taking all factors into consideration this was the county's worst snowstorm since the legendary January 1881 when the winds may have blown even stronger and the snow lay deeper.

Virtually every mechanical digger, bull dozer and farm tractor in the county were used to clear snow away following the memorable blizzard of February 1978 as here in East Stour.

A massive snowdrift at Yetminster in February 1978.

This desolate scene is just below the Square and Compass Public House at Worth Matravers where in a cutting, the snow had drifted 8 to 9 feet deep in February 1978. A sign post on the left is just poking out of the snow.

The great storm but a sunny finale

The Dorset coast took a battering during the storms and floods of 1978 and 1979 and here at West Bay repairs costing £600,000 are taking place and were needed when in December 1981 another furious gale struck.

1980

A dry April and May with a virtually unbroken spell of sunshine from 11th to 17th. From the 9th to the 19th sunshine averaged 11 hours a day.

September was warmer than June and July.

A virtually unique burst of cold air from the east so early in the season gave snow across the county on the 5th with day temperatures not far off freezing. South of Dorset, across the Channel, Jersey experienced several inches of snow lying on the ground.

1981

A very wet March at Dorchester with 7.87 inches of rain but the main event of the Spring was a late snow storm especially so on the Dorset hills. In a cold northerly airstream an area of low pressure swung southeast over Wales and England. Up to four inches fell on the 25th April but on Salisbury Plain there were ferocious conditions with 300 travellers trapped in 70 cars and coaches. They had to be rescued by the police and army. The thick, clinging snow caused

One driver found the conditions near Christchurch far too hazardous on Sunday 13th December 1981.

power lines to topple and at Sherborne the lights went out at the Yeatman hospital while a woman was in labour. Torches were used until emergency generators could be brought into action.

Electricity failure also meant problems at Evershot where at one farm eight piglets died when the infra red lights faded out. The baby pigs had sought warmth under their mother but were crushed as she rolled on them. Over 1,500 homes were without power for up to 15 hours with Stourpaine being one of the worst affected areas.

A coach load of darts players returning to Devon from a tournament in France were marooned as their vehicle was overwhelmed on Abbotsbury Hill. They were forced to spend most of the day in the village. Another casualty was the abandonment of the Dorset Police Special Constabulary Competition held at Wareham.

Elsewhere the extreme conditions led to a first class cricket match being called off because it was too cold at Fenners, Cambridge.

December proved the coldest so far this century. Heavy snow in the southeast on the 11th caused Bournemouth's Hurn airport to look more like a major international airport as many planes were diverted there from Heathrow and Gatwick.

The main event took place on Sunday 13th after minus 13F was recorded at Shawbury, Shropshire, an English record. A deep low crossed southern England causing a blizzard during the morning which by afternoon fortunately had turned to rain. Thirty people had to be rescued from an Ecuadorian freighter, the 10,000 ton Bonita, listing in mountainous seas at an angle of 45 degrees off Portland Bill. A huge wave generated by winds reported at 92mph along the Dorset coast swept a fisherman to his death from the Cobb at Lyme Regis.

At Highcliffe several residents in a block of flats on the sea front were evacuated as the roof was peeled back by the storm force wind.

On land there were widespread power cuts causing two thirds of Wessex Water's pumping stations to fail and there were over 200 breaks of power. Many trees were brought down in the county and elsewhere in Britain the Advanced Passenger Train faltered 20 miles south of Glasgow in the freezing conditions and the Queen herself took shelter in a small hotel at Old Sodbury, Avon as her Range Rover became snow bound. At Christchurch there was widespread flooding as the Stour burst its banks due to melting snow and heavy rain.

The summer of 1983 was very warm especially July which was the warmest month ever recorded in UK records. There were some thunderstorms triggered by the heat as here near Verwood on the 23rd June.

1982

During a severe cold spell Braemar, Grampian, equalled on the 10th January the lowest ever recorded temperature in Britain of minus 17F. The other occasion was 11th February 1895. Newport in Shropshire set a new English record of minus 15F. It was not as cold in Dorset but temperatures sank to below 10F in several places.

Heavy snow fell on the 8th January giving a five inch cover and Weymouth was virtually cut off for a time and in north Dorset most main roads were blocked by drifts over four feet.

On the 11th/12th July there were severe thunderstorms with large hail at Corfe Mullen. Lightning flashed by the second and thunder rumbled for 11 hours at Shillingstone. 2.95 inches of rain was measured at Marnhull.

1983

Extraordinary thunderstorms occurred on Sunday 5th June. Four major storms followed an east-north-east track from Lyme Bay bringing hail as large as tennis balls, day darkness, gale force gusts of wind, flash flooding and even lumps of coal and coke dropping on to garden lawns. One garden received 92 lumps. Tornadoes embedded in the storm were responsible for this manifestation, the tornado responsible probably having crossed a site west of Wareham where coal and coke were stored. The lifeboat at Poole was launched to tow a 15-foot fishing boat struck by lightning a mile off shore.

July was the warmest on record across England back at least to the middle of the seventeenth century and the warmest of any previous summer month. Maximum temperatures averaged over 80F with a mean temperature of 68.6F at Dorchester. Extreme maximum temperatures were not outstanding but 89.5F was recorded in the Bournemouth area on 12th. It was the sheer persistence of warmth that brought it such an accolade.

1984

The cricket season got off to a splendid start for April was a magnificent month; sunny, dry and warm with record breaking numbers of guests in Bournemouth's hotels. Easter was the warmest since 1949. On the 22nd 74F was widely measured and there was an absolute drought for 26 days during the month.

No rain was recorded after the 6th in June and both July and August were dry and warm. The period April-September experienced the lowest rainfall since 1921. Concern over the lack of rain led to the Environment Minister, Ian Gow, responsible for water supplies, to visit the West Country and the Minister had to seek shelter as torrential rain fell!

On the 19th July Dorset was on the edge of a powerful earth tremor centred on North Wales.

On Boxing Day hail half an inch in diameter fell in Bournemouth and at Charmouth an inch of hail lay on road and pavements.

1985

The coldest January since 1963 with snow on the ground from the 8th to the 20th, five inches deep at Wraxall on the 8th and eight inches on the 18th. On the latter date over 100 schools were shut due to the difficult conditions as was Hurn Airport. Police warned parents in Christchurch to stop their children from skating on the thin ice covering the harbour.

A depression moving into France brought the heavy snow on the 18th blocking some routes such as the A350 Shaftesbury to Warminster Road. There was tragedy too as a man drowned in the River Stour at Sturminster Newton attempting to rescue his Labrador dog which had fallen through ice. It was reported by the Dorset Echo that Pallington lakes at Tincleton were frozen over for the first time since 1979.

October laid claim to the best month of the year with temperatures reaching 76F on the 1st and no rain after the 8th but November was the coldest since 1952.

Christmas Day was not the traditional white but had a very soggy appearance as over two inches of rain fell in many places with 2.3 inches at Forde Abbey as a depression crossed southern England.

1986

February was the second coldest of the century. An exceptional feature of the month was the wind which blew constantly from the quarter north through to east with a complete absence of air from any other direction. There was little snow and it was the driest since 1965. This led to a heath blaze at Studland on the 27th.

The temperature fell to just 14F on the 10th in the Compton Valence area but rather more unusually the temperature throughout February failed to rise above 40F in most areas.

It was not the best of summers and it ended on a dramatic note with ex-hurricane Charley regenerating itself with vigour as it crossed the Atlantic. Losing energy after mauling North Carolina it activated just in time to wash out the August Bank Holiday on the 25th. Frome St Quentin measured 2.46 inches of rain. Ian Botham had just scored 24 off one over at the Oval Test against New Zealand when play was abandoned. The day is often packed with outside events such as Dorchester's Big Affair. The thousands of people who normally turn up stayed at home with only a handful braving the lashing rain and gales. It led also to the cancellation of Weymouth's Fireworks Spectacular from Spain. Many trees toppled and a land slip blocked the Broadwindsor to Netherbury road. Along the coast boats were battered and set adrift as huge seas pounded the shore. Fifteen vessels in Poole Harbour were damaged and there was the usual crop of foolhardy folk who disregarded the signs and took to the water. Three young men were rescued at the mouth of Weymouth Harbour as their craft broke its rudder causing it to flounder in the heavy swell.

1987

Dorset escaped the worst of the deep snows which isolated many parts of eastern Britain between 11th and the 18th January but it was extremely cold. With a top temperature at Shillingstone of just 23F it was the coldest day of the century. One Bournemouth camping equipment retailer sold out of thermal vests, gloves and long-johns.

The year of course is best known for the Great October Storm. East of Weymouth a tumult of wind devastated the countryside. A gust of 100mph was measured at Portland and after midnight in just the space of a few hours, 75,000 homes were left without power, buildings collapsed and trees fell in their thousands. Death followed as a tree crashed on to a fire engine whose crew had just answered a false alarm, the bell having been triggered by the furious winds. Two of the fire officers were crushed to death as the appliance passed along Lymington Road, Christchurch. Almost overlooked in all the pandemonium were the incredible pressure rises as the depression responsible moved away northeast having traversed Devon. A rise of 0.8 inches [26 millibars] took place in four hours, probably unique in southern England.

Snow drifts with cornices alongside a road at East Stour on the 14th January 1987.

The Panacea being winched from Kimmerbridge Ledges by a Chinook helicopter after breaking her moorings in Portland Harbour during a gale on 13th November 1987. This was a major operation as the helicopter had been chartered from Scotland and the boat itself had to be stripped of fittings to reduce weight.

1988

A virtually snowless year with rainfall below average by around nine per cent. There was no rain at all for 26 consecutive days in June in Weymouth. However it was certainly wet and quite stormy at times earlier in the year. January had no settled spells with high pressure, rather a constant stream of depressions roaring in from the Atlantic. On the 4th part of the sea front was closed as storm waves sliced out a 60 foot length of the promenade at Gordon Steps, Southbourne. Another hole appeared at Fisherman's Walk. Rainfall approached eight inches in parts of the county.

What a contrast to end the year, December brought a very unusual combination of dry yet mild weather with exceptionally high pressure. There were few frosts and no snow and the barometer often read above 30.4 inches.

1989

A year of particular interest. It was the warmest year of the century and Bournemouth enjoyed 2,092 hours of sun, the second sunniest behind 1911.

The period November 1988 to the end of January 1989 was the driest since 1879. February was the mildest since 1945 and an extraordinarily deep low pressure area crossed Dorset with a central depth of 27.7 inches [948.8mb] probably the lowest pressure since Christmas 1821.

May was the driest since 1896 and the mercury rose to 83F on the 24th. The hot weather set off some severe thunderstorms in north Dorset during the day. Hailstones the size of marbles fell at Shaftesbury perforating plastic sheeting and making a sorry mess of vegetables and flowers. Hail lay six inches deep in places. Premises were flooded in Gillingham as almost a month's rain, 2.4 inches, cascaded down in just 100 minutes.

July was the driest since 1934 and the mercury climbed to 88F. In fact during the summer the mercury stopped 70F on 69 days in the Dorchester area compared to 71 in 1976. Britain's 400 vineyards started harvesting a month early.

These beach huts took a battering from the elements at Southbourne in December 1989, a far cry from the lazy, hazy days of the summer that year.

The Weymouth district, suffering from hose pipe and sprinkler bans, was lashed by a thunderstorm producing 1.2 inches of rain on the 11th September. It was just hours after Apache, Setter Mani, a Red Indian rain dancer appeared on Granada Television. He was dancing on a weather map gyrating up and down across the Weymouth area.

Rain came with a vengeance accompanied by stormy conditions. On the 21st a squall line of showers bred a fully fledged tornado which descended on the village of West Stour. In the space of a few seconds many farm buildings were flattened, trees uprooted and telephone lines sent crashing to the ground. One of the saddest casualties was the crushing of a newly restored Rolls Royce and Mercedes convertible at Church Farm. A barn collapsed as massive roof beams were wrenched apart and carried 400 yards into fields. The cost was put at £100,000. At East Stour a radio enthusiast's 50 foot aerial designed to survive winds of 150mph was blown down. A local farmer who saw the tornado described it thus, "As it approached it was twisting and looked like a ball of fire". A 300-year-old barn was smashed to pieces.

Along the coast there was extensive flooding with thousands of pounds worth of damage to homes in the Green and Stanley Road areas of Poole. It was particularly harrowing as the scummy water invaded just before Christmas. Boats sunk in the harbour as winds touched 80mph and fallen trees blocked roads in the Corfe Mullen area. And everywhere burglar alarms wailed and whined triggered by the storms.

One 90-year-old Christchurch widow slept blissfully in her bed whilst rising flood waters swirled around it. She was rescued by her son and daughter at 3.30am having had to break into her house. Unfortunately the old lady lost her false teeth as she was carried from the building.

At Mudeford Quay the storm waves engulfed the entire sea wall flooding cottages and the lifeboat station. The Isle of Portland was cut off for six hours by storm waves pounding the causeway.

The remains of a barn at Church Farm, West Stour, after a tornado ripped through the district on the 12th December 1989. Inside the building was stored a Mercedes Convertible and a Rolls Royce and damage to the vehicles amounted to £100,000.

The day it rained coal and coke

A FINE day was in prospect on Sunday 5th June 1983. The barometer was set fair and it seemed ideal for a family outing or some leisurely gardening. But every so often Mother Nature conspires to produce a surprise or two and 5th June was to be one of those days.

In spite of high pressure at the surface the atmosphere was cooling high above Dorset, due to what meteorologists call an upper air trough. This moved slowly southeast, forcing air ahead of it, upwards. By 11.15am with no warnings given by earlier weather forecasts the somewhat surprised folk of south Dorset were being treated to the first of a series of severe thunderstorms that were to cross the area during the day.

The sky turned black as the darkest night making some people feel the end of the world was nigh. Then a sudden squall brought near gale force winds with lashing rain and golf ball sized hail.

At Osmington near Weymouth one householder counted 67 holes in his sun lounge roof. Nearby at Warmwell a farmer looked on in horror as his entire crop of lettuces valued at £5,000 was completely shredded in a matter of minutes. It brought mayhem to yachtsmen with the hailstones sinking boats in the harbour at Christchurch and the Poole lifeboat was launched to rescue two men in a fishing boat struck by lightning off Bournemouth.

The storms brought three inches of rain to Winfrith and at Preston on lower ground, on the outskirts of Weymouth, floodwater reached five feet in depth. At the Radipole Nature Reserve up to 700 birds' nests were destroyed by the combination of heavy rain and the large hail.

In Bournemouth and Poole hailstones attained the size of hens' eggs but even more remarkable was the fact that many people found their gardens littered with coal and coke. One lady picked up 92 pieces and some were embedded in hail suggesting it had spent some time within the cloud and had been carried to a great height. Along the River Frome the pear-shaped hail and coke caused a herd of cattle to stampede and nearby a lady was bruised trying to rescue a tortoise from her garden. Much greenhouse glass was shattered and lean-tos punctured.

The question people naturally asked was, "How did the coal and coke hitch a ride in a cloud?" The Tornado and Storm Research Organization based at Oxford Brookes University carried out an investigation and concluded that the foreign bodies had probably been lifted from an old industrial site west of Wareham by a tornado embedded in the most violent part of the storm.

Towering cumulo-nimbus clouds like this one off Portland Bill can produce hail and thunder and sometimes tornados. The instrument in the foreground is a Campbell Stokes Sunshine Recorder. It recorded 331 hours of sunshine during July 1976.

The unexpected thunderstorms on Sunday 5th June 1983 led to flash floods that produced quite a hazard for pedestrians as here in the centre of Charminster.

Dorset first in the firing line

These greenhouses at Hill View Nurseries near Wareham were no match for the wind hammering past at 100 mph after midnight on the 16th October 1987.

A RAPIDLY deepening area of low pressure flung itself upon the Dorset coast around 2pm on the 16th October 1987. It had already brought havoc to the Channel Islands and Brittany but Dorset was first in the firing line when it reached the mainland. The storm with 100 miles per hour winds was to topple some 15 million trees, take 18 lives and cause over two and a half thousand million pounds worth of damage. Although most of its venom was aimed at counties south and east of London it cut a swathe of destruction across the east of Dorset.

Caravans were picked up like matchboxes, roof tiles and even entire roofs blew away, power cables came crashing down cutting current to 25,000 homes and causing water pumping stations to fail. Trees splintered and fell.

In Swanage 72 school children were rescued at a caravan site as the caravans began to cartwheel, whilst in Bournemouth pensioners in a block of flats escaped as the roof began to tear apart. Within minutes of them leaving, heavy 15 foot roof beams came crashing down onto bedrooms where residents had been sleeping. At Highcliffe similar scenes were enacted with one 87 year old sitting on the floor whilst being showered with plaster and splintered wood. She could not open her door as it had jammed and was rescued by a 76 year old friend who was given 'super human strength' when hearing her pleas for help. She heaved against the door forcing it open.

The former Mayor of Christchurch had to flee from another block of flats leaving behind all her possessions. A friend managed to rescue an illuminated scroll honouring her freedom of the borough and

Looking down on the Greystones flats, at Highcliffe after the roof had been removed by hurricane force gusts of wind during the night of 15th/16th October 1987.

also a photograph of her in mayoral robes.

Tragedy struck in the early hours as a fire engine was being driven along Lymington Road, Highcliffe, answering one of many emergency calls. It turned out to be a false alarm set off by the gale. Just as the appliance passed, a terrific gust of wind sent a massive tree toppling to the ground instantly crushing to death two firemen in the cab, Graham White and David Gregory, and slightly injuring four other crew. Both the dead men were volunteer firemen.

Mountainous waves, lashing spray and hurricane force winds made being at sea a nightmare. The catamaran Sunbeam Chaser on its way to warmer West Indian climes ran into trouble off Portland. The Weymouth lifeboat rescued the five crew who had jumped overboard from the floundering vessel. The destroyer HMS Birmingham, sister ship to the Sheffield and Coventry, lost in the Falklands conflict, placed herself to the windward in order to protect the rescue operation. It also spread oil on the sea to stifle the waves.

The wind had increased steadily from being flat calm at 10pm and the temperature had actually risen during the evening to a very balmy 59F by midnight. Warm air from Biscay and Spain was being hurled northeastwards whilst cool air plunged southwards and helped in the rapid deepening of this powerful vortex. Trees still had a canopy of leaves whilst the ground was waterlogged from frequent deluges in the days before the storm arrived. Both these factors had a major bearing on why so many trees fell.

Between 4am and 7am the barometer at Portland Naval Base rose 0.74 inches (25.4 millibars) the largest three hour rise ever recorded within the British Isles. At Hurn pressure soared 12 millibars in just one hour, regarded by meteorologists as being a 1 in 500 year event.

Looking like the aftermath of a huge bomb explosion the 1987 Storm wrought death and destruction to Highcliffe.

Another big storm but record-breaking warmth

Taking to high ground at Mudeford Quay during a stormy day in 1992.

1990

This was another record-breaking year with much outstanding weather. The winter was very stormy and mild, February proving the second warmest over England as a whole since 1659 and it was the wettest winter of the century along the coast.

An intense area of low pressure crossed southern Scotland on the 25th and became known as the Burns' Day Storm. Forty-seven people died across England and Wales as a result of a tight pressure gradient on its southern flank producing storm force winds. Gusts reached 77mph at King's Park, Bournemouth, the highest speed since the first readings in 1900 and 85mph was measured on an anemometer in Dorchester.

Spring was the sunniest of the century so far, the driest since 1938 and the warmest since 1948. In contrast June was the dullest this century with only 143 hours of bright sunshine at Bournemouth.

It was back to almost Mediterranean weather in July and August with 332 hours of sunshine in July, the second sunniest behind 381 hours in 1911. The heat intensified to bring Dorset its county record on the 3rd August with 95F at Dorchester. A Caribbean turtle, six feet by seven, drawn north by the unusually warm sea was seen feeding off the coast on jellyfish. Hundreds of stinging tropical jellyfish up to two feet across were jamming fishermen's nets in Studland Bay.

Although mostly warm conditions prevailed during the year, on the 28th September the temperature fell to 29.5F at Hurn, lower than most of the winter. It proved to be the coldest September night for 50 years.

1991

Just 12F was recorded at Bournemouth on the 8th February and a veil of snow covered the ground during the second week.

Most parts had the driest May of the century with less than 0.2 inches. No rain at all fell from 8th May to the 3rd June. What a contrast to June which was cool and wet. One south coast hotel was offering guests sun lamps.

September it is said can "dry up the wells or break down the bridges". Sometimes the warm sea temperatures of early autumn can produce large falls of rain. This year was a good example with 4.36 inches measured in 24 hours at Poole on 28th September and Puddletown lived up to its name with 3.52 inches. The wet weather was due to a deep depression moving southeast into Biscay.

A giant mudslide triggered by the rains swept down Middle Chine and tore away part of the West Overcliffe Drive, Westbourne, and carried off two 30-foot trees hundreds of yards down the Chine.

At least fishermen were pleased as trout ponds in the county were refilling after drying out following the dry winter.

The frozen River Frome at Wareham during the second week of February 1991.

The local stream at Winfrith Newburgh rose seven feet in just 20 minutes following heavy rain on the 30th December 1993 flooding the road through the village.

1992

The end of March brought an unusually sharp thunderstorm as a low pressure area sat over central southern England. A bungalow at Hengistbury Head was struck by lightning sending the chimney hurtling through the living room just after 9pm. Another chimney crashed onto the roof of a block of flats after being hit by lightning at Southborne.

A very warm May, only 1989 having higher average temperatures. Temperatures exceeded 80F on the 23rd and the dry conditions prompted honorary Red Indian John Morley to do a rain dance round his Bournemouth garden. He had good reason for some of Dorset's rivers were on the government's list of waterways suffering most from drought such as the Wey, Piddle and Allen. Water restrictions were placed on 120,000 people in the Lyme Regis and East Devon area in early June.

The Empire State Building in New York has been struck 20 times during the same storm but just two flashes were enough for Mr Simon Clifford. He was sitting with his wife in the kitchen of his cottage at Manswood when a flash of lightning struck the cooker. They fled to the living room and another brilliant flash of lightning severed the electricity. Mr and Mrs Clifford escaped in the family car to Blandford.

After a wet November with nearly seven inches of rain in places the Wey, Allen and Piddle rivers came off the government's critical list of drought-affected rivers.

1993

A mild January but the impression was not gained of a pleasant month as it was both wet and very dull with only around 33 hours of sunshine, the second dullest in over 100 years. February had an unusual combination of being dry but mild. Barometers averaged over 30.4 inches, extremely high.

Nearly 13 inches of rain fell in the Dorchester area after the first week of September to the 13th October.

A remarkably low temperature of just 14.5F was recorded on 23rd November in Dorchester. Bournemouth experienced its lowest November night temperature of 16F, and by day did not rise above 30F. Did the old adage of "If ice on a pond in November can bear the weight of a duck, the winter will only have slush and muck", meaning a mild winter, come true? Yes, the winter was mild but a small low in a cold northwesterly airstream produced light snow on Christmas Day about an inch deep in places to give a white Christmas.

Mild weather soon returned and it was rain that caused problems on the 30th. Swanage was cut off by floodwater as 1.7 inches of rain fell in just eight hours and water was three feet deep in Wool. At Winfrith Newburgh the local stream rose about seven feet in 20 minutes or so.

During the summer it is sand castles that can provide the fun but occasionally snow is exciting on the beach as here in Bournemouth, mid February 1994.

1994

An extremely wet winter. At Dorchester where 19.83 inches of rain was measured it was the wettest for 100 years. The observer, Mr John Oliver, stated that there were no two consecutive dry days.

It snowed for some ten hours on the 14th February giving a cover of six inches in the Purbeck area. The maximum temperature on the 14th was only 27F at Winfrith.

During a very unsettled end to March a vigorous low pressure area moved east across England on the 31st and generated a tornado that was featured on local television news 'Meridian Tonight'. With a sound like an express train it roared across Lulworth Cove tearing a 20sq foot piece of roofing from the Lulworth Cove Hotel and propelled cars across the car park before disappearing over a hill.

It was another warm year, exceptionally so in November as it averaged the warmest over England since 1659. There were 23 days when the mercury surpassed 54F and nine exceeded 59F. However the mild air was very moist and cloud-laden and the November total of bright sunshine measured only 32 hours, the lowest on record.

Surging through the floodwater at Three Legged Cross, January 1994, during the wettest winter for 100 years in parts of Dorset.

1995

The combined January and February rainfall amounted to as much as 14 inches, the highest value since at least 1900.

With low pressure just to the south of Dorset on the 22nd April a plane had to make an emergency landing at Bournemouth Airport after being struck by lightning.

A tee shirt and shorts summer, the warmest of the century. August 1995 ranks top in the temperature league back to 1659 across England. The heat and drought led to many heathland fires and they were having a serious effect on wild life. Canford Heath suffered six serious blazes within a week in early August. Smooth snakes, sand lizards and nightjars were high on the casualty list. The area was only just recovering after the conflagrations in 1976. One blaze involved 100 fire fighters and many were thought to have been started deliberately.

At East Stour the mercury reached 92.4F on the 3rd and in the Purbeck area the thermometer touched 86F on 22 days during the summer.

October continued the warmth with it too ranking as the warmest ever measured over England. A reading of 75F was recorded at Winfrith as late as the 8th.

"Fowl" weather at Christchurch Quay during the wet winter of 1995.

July 1997 was very dry and sunny and ideal haymaking weather near Tolpuddle taken on the 19th.

1996

Not a very promising start to the year with the dullest January on record. Even if one was lucky the sun was seen for only an average of 50 minutes a day but at least the summer was above par in the sunshine stakes.

May was the coolest since 1902 in some parts with day temperatures only 45F on the 18th. At the Chelsea Flower Show there was a dearth of spring blooms.

A heat wave on the 7th June was followed later in the day by spectacular thunderstorms that produced damaging hailstones. Car bodies were pitted and conservatories shattered.

Hurricane Lili which had caused much damage to Cuban sugar cane plantations, had almost dissipated in mid-Atlantic before heading northeastwards. It reinvigorated as it crossed central Britain on the 28th October. Winds peaked on its southern flank at 70mph and the Cobb at Lyme Regis was closed as massive storm waves broke against it.

After the glorious weather of July 1997 there was a temporary set back for holidaymakers in early August when a boat was more a suitable mode of transport in the Pleasure Gardens at Bournemouth. In the north of the county at Shaftesbury nearly 4 inches of rain fell from the 3rd to the 6th.

June 1997 was very unsettled and this lady is battling with the elements at Sandbanks.

1997

It was a cold January, a rarity in recent years, but very little snow lay and the mild weather returned by February.

March was the warmest since 1957 in Dorchester.

April was very sunny and at Bournemouth the second sunniest since 1893 with an average of eight hours 36 minutes per day. At night it was excellent comet viewing weather with a clear view of Hal Bopp. However the old adage "clear moon, frost soon" came true on the night of the 21st. Values as low as 22F were measured and damage to plants was considerable.

Only 0.15 inches of rain fell at Winfrith Newburgh during July and with 285 sunny hours beaches were packed at Bournemouth and Weymouth.

Then came one of those notorious pendulum swings of weather making it a nightmare for holiday makers. Thick cloud brought heavy rain during the first week of August flooding Bournemouth's Central Gardens. Many places experienced at least three inches of rain. Nature then relented and there was a good deal of fine and very warm weather and nights were especially balmy. In places August rivalled the record-breaking 1995 for temperature.

September brought sparkling weather with temperatures often in the seventies with quiet conditions, a case of "September blow soft til the fruits in the loft". As late as the 19th October 70F was recorded at several places including Winfrith in Purbeck but the month ended with sharp frosts.

Bournemouth beach on the 20th July. With 285 sunny hours at Bournemouth and hardly any rain July 1997 supplied ideal holiday weather.

Burns' Day Mayhem

IT SEEMED almost unthinkable that another storm would strike southern England when the memories of October 1987 were still fresh in many folk's minds. Foresters and National Trust wardens were still clearing up after the "storm of a lifetime". December 1989 was very unsettled but by Christmas it had quietened down. Would it be a peaceful January? For a while it was.

However during the early morning of Thursday 25th January grim storm warnings flashed across TV screens. Two days earlier a somewhat trifling area of low pressure lay off the eastern seaboard of North America. Unfortunately it was embedded under a particularly powerful jet stream where some six miles up winds reached 200mph. Very cold polar air was being flung south into the heated Gulf Stream waters of the North Atlantic and within 36 hours a major storm had been generated. It had been successfully forecast but nonetheless it was still shockingly sudden and destructive. Unlike 1987 it occurred during the working day and the affected area was far greater. The centre of the low moved eastwards close to Ayr where on this day in 1759 the celebrated Scottish poet Robert Burns was born.

During Thursday morning winds steadily increased with gusts exceeding hurricane force up to 85mph at Dorchester and 77mph in Bournemouth, the latter's highest speed since the Weather Station commenced in 1900. In the Bournemouth area alone millions of pounds worth of damage was caused but on a more tragic note elsewhere in the county lives were lost in a tumult of toppled trees, crushed cars and smashed buildings.

A Poole man, Ray Farnden, was killed whilst restoring the fire-damaged stately house at Uppark, Hampshire. Together with his colleague from Ringwood he was packing up after being advised to leave due to the worsening weather conditions. Suddenly a temporary roof structure was bodily lifted from its supports by a terrific gust of wind. It hurtled onto the men below. The alarm was raised with some difficulty as many telephone lines were severed and the rescue services were hampered by the numerous fallen trees.

The 1990 storm affected all parts of Dorset and damage was widespread. This crushed car was pictured in Bournemouth.

The entire roof was blown off this maisonette in Winton during the Burn's Day Storm of January 25th 1990.

In Swanage a 78 year old pensioner, John Green, died when he was blown over and a lady from Sturminster Newton was killed as her car crashed into a tree which had fallen across the main Blandford-Poole road at Charlton Marshall. Nationally 47 people lost their lives.

The perilous conditions led to ambulance men abandoning their industrial action and all crew including those off-duty sprung into action. And they were needed. One man was lucky to escape with just minor cuts when a four foot wide skylight plummeted 25 foot at Blandford United Reform Church. At the same time a 15 foot gable wall fell from the building. Mr Ronald White the caretaker was hit on the head by the flying debris. Another man was more seriously injured when a pole fell on him at Hinton St Mary and a dislodged roof tile knocked a council workman unconscious in Wareham. One famous person injured in the storm was the TV star of 'Allo, 'Allo, Gordon Kaye, who suffered a severe head wound when a tree hit his car in London.

Not one but three trees were hurled onto a house at Inverclyde Road, Parkstone, crushing the lounge but miraculously the two occupants had just left the room. In another incident a giant 70 foot eucalyptus tree crashed through a roof of a bungalow in Creekmore Lane, Poole and knocked down a complete garden wall as well.

The entire roof was blown off a Winton maisonette in Wimborne Road and worse followed as it landed on the family's car damaging it beyond repair.

This car was crushed at Springbourne when winds gusted to nearly 80 mph on January 25th 1990.

A number of Dorset commuters who work in London were forced to stay in the Capital overnight as virtually all its mainline stations shut down.

At Stoborough Green a terrified horse missed certain death by inches. It became trapped when three massive trees fell onto the rear of the stables. The rescue services worked as the storm raged, finally releasing the petrified beast called Fancy Money with just a few scratches.

The countryside suffered badly with 20 of the historic Badbury Rings beech trees poleaxed. On Brownsea Island 200 trees fell. Nationally around five million trees were brought down. Farmers already beset by a milk crisis and Mad Cow Disease faced a further predicament as electricity supplies were cut and cows had to be milked by hand, no mean feat when there is a herd of over 250 animals. Keeping the milk cool was also a desperate problem. Even by Saturday there were 40,000 Dorset homes without electricity and emergency repair teams came from as far away as Scotland to help out. A casualty of the power cuts was the BBC's Songs of Praise programme due to be held at Wimborne Minster. It was rescheduled.

Horticulturists were faced with their entire crop in ruins. Polytunnels were no match for the 80 miles an hour winds and winter crops such as chrysanthemums, carnations, lettuces and tomatoes did not take kindly to being exposed to the elements.

The 1990 storm destroyed 5 million trees across England and Wales to add to the 15 million lost in 1987. These two toppled onto houses in New Road, West Parley.

The winter of 1989/90 was one of the stormiest ever recorded in the UK with over £2.5 thousand million pounds worth of insured losses such as the car in the above picture at Colonnade Road, Pokesdown. It was also extremely mild and winds blew almost constantly in from the southwest bringing very wet weather at times. Floodwaters can be seen in the picture below during February in King's Road, Swanage.

The Sherborne Hailstorm

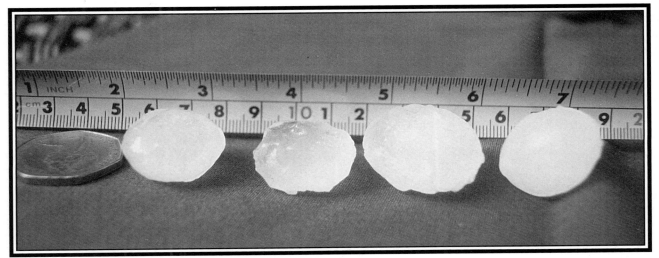

Giant hailstones that fell in Sherborne during the evening of the 7th June 1996.

NOW and then Dorset can lie on the boundary between cooler air moving off the Atlantic and stifling hot winds from the continent. This was the weather situation on Friday 7th June 1996. Temperatures rose to 82F in Bournemouth during the afternoon though places in eastern England topped 90F.

Co-author Ian Currie had driven from South Wales during the morning, where it was chilly and wet. He was dressed in a jacket with the car heater switched on!

The afternoon sky across Dorset became increasingly threatening as the cooler air to the west travelled eastwards. Ahead of it the lighter warm air was pushed upwards, a classic thunderstorm situation.

At first no storms materialized and the early evening was warm and humid, but by 7.30pm a dark wall of cloud approached from the west. It was about this time that Ted Braunholtz at his home in Sherborne, heard a rushing sound, whilst his neighbour described it as roaring like an express train. This clamour lasted for some minutes before it was joined by the clatter of breaking glass and shattered plastic roofing. Giant hailstones fell in a five minute destructive spree.

Motorists were forced to stop suddenly and some of those who failed to find shelter for their cars faced the prospect of insurance claims of up to £1,500. Bonnets, roofs and wings were pitted by the icy missiles. Ted described the stones as being elongated, the biggest about two inches lengthways though near his house they were around one inch. In many places they were described as "shapeless chunks of ice" or "like ice cubes", some parts had roundish stones mixed with some lumps of ice.

Another observer, a Mr Ball, described what was in all probability a mini tornado. An ominous almost roof-top black cloud swirled just to the west of his house attended by a mighty roaring sound. A sudden wind raised papers and leaves higher than the house and the loose material swirled across seven adjacent gardens. Then down came the hail.

Elsewhere in Dorset it was not a night for the faint-hearted. At Winfrith the Police Headquarters was struck by lightning, crippling communications for at least four hours and at Motcombe lightning struck a pole-mounted transformer, disabling power supplies to 3,000 homes. In the Poole area a house was damaged and chimneys were shattered at Swanage, but it was just into Devon where a house in Seaton was badly damaged. Part of its roof was blown away and two children narrowly escaped injury. Nearby in Axminster an angler was knocked unconscious by a flash of lightning as he ran to his car to shelter from the storm. Probably his heavy duty, rubber-soled Wellington boots prevented serious wounds.

Window on the Weather

THERE can be few better places to observe the weather than on the Isle of Portland. This virtually treeless mass of limestone rock set into the Channel is an ideal observation dome. At the southern end, on the bill itself, there has been a lighthouse since 1716.

The Old Higher Lighthouse went out of service in 1906 but is now the home of Fran Lockyer. She used to work as an auxiliary coastguard lookout but when the meteorological station and coastguard was due to be closed in 1992 she recognized its importance and carried on the observations.

Five daily sets of readings are sent to Bracknell, part of the weather station being automatic such as air pressure, temperature wind speed and direction but Fran records the sunshine, cloud types, visibility, weather conditions and even the state of the ground be it wet, dry, frozen or snow covered.

Fran's good sense of observation led her to witness one of nature's most awesome sights, a waterspout which passed close to the headland itself on the morning of the 12th September 1993. Fran grabbed her camera and took the stunning shot which is displayed on the back cover of this book.

Fran Lockyer who runs the Portland Bill Weather Station for the Meteorological Office. She is beside a Stevenson Screen, a louvred weather instrument container designed by Robert Loius Stevenson's father, Thomas. Fran took the dramatic waterspout pictured on page 54 from her station in 1993.

A street of cumulus cloud over Portland. The island is providing uplift to form the cloud.

The Weather Station at Swanage. It is one of the sunniest locations within the British Isles with an average of 1760 hours of bright sunshine a year. By comparison London has about 1514 hours.

CLIMATE DATA FOR BOURNEMOUTH

Month	Average daily max. temperature	Average daily min. temperature	Average monthly rainfall in inches	Average sunshine totals in hours
	°F	°F		
January	45.4	36.5	3.6	65
February	45.7	35.8	2.5	81
March	49.3	38.2	2.5	133
April	54.2	40.3	1.9	184
May	59.9	45.7	2.1	218
June	65.5	51.1	2.0	230
July	69.3	54.3	1.5	211
August	68.8	54.3	2.2	207
September	64.8	50.9	2.6	151
October	58.9	47.0	3.0	116
November	51.3	40.3	3.3	71
December	47.2	38.4	3.5	56
Total	56.7 av.	44.4 av.	30.7	1,723

CONVERSION TABLE FROM BRITISH TO METRIC [SI] UNITS

British Units	Metric [SI] Units
one inch	25.54 mm
one inch	2.54 cm
one foot	0.3048 metres (m)
one yard	0.9144 metres
one mile	1.6093 kilo m
one pint	0.5682 litres
one gallon	4.5459 litres
one ounce	28.3495 grams (g)
one pound	453.592 grams
one pound	0.4535 kilo g
one ton	1.0160 tonne
one acre	0.4047 hectares

CONVERSION CHART: FAHRENHEIT TO CELSIUS

F	-22	-13	-4	0	5	14	23	32	41	50	59	68	77	86	95	104
C	-30	-25	-20	-18	15	-10	-5	0	5	10	15	20	25	30	35	40

THE HIGHS AND LOWS OF DORSET'S WEATHER

Hottest Day 94.3F at Fontmell Magna 3rd August 1990 95F Dorchester There were seven consecutive days above 90F 26th June to 2nd July 1976.	**Sunniest Year** 2,137 hours of sun at Bournemouth in 1911.	**Sunniest Month** 381 hours in Bournemouth July 1911.
Coldest Night 6.8F at Poole 2nd January 1979 though unofficially 0F at Wimborne St Giles January 1945	**Coldest Winter** The 1962/63 winter was the coldest since 1740. At Shaftesbury it averaged just 30.2F Dec. to Feb.	**Warmest Month** July 1983 with an average of 68.3F at Dorchester.
Wettest Day 11.0 inches 18th July 1955 at Martinstown.	**Snowiest Winter** The ground was snow-covered for 69 days during the winter of 1962/63 at Shaftesbury.	**Dullest Year** 1,445 hours of sunshine only at Bournemouth in 1932.
Wettest Year 60.2 inches at Cerne Abbas in 1872.	**Driest Year** 13.47 inches at Portland Bill Lighthouse in 1921.	**Windiest Day** 102 mph 17th January 1965 Portland.

About the Authors

Mark Ching

Mark's fascination with the weather stems from tales told by his great grandmother of the legendary blizzard of 1881. His own experience of the blistering 1976 summer and ferocious blizzard of February 1978 served to stimulate his interest in weather history even further.

Born in Bournemouth in 1960 he was educated at Bournemouth School for Boys before leaving in 1976 to become a thatcher, a craft that has provided ample opportunity for Mark to study the skies of Dorset for over 20 years.

Mark has written about the weather for the *Wessex Journal* and *Dorset Life* magazines and has weekly columns in the Dorchester and Wareham *Guardians* as well as a regular feature in Bournemouth's *Daily Echo* newspaper.

Mark is married to Julie, a remedial masseuse and aromatherapist and they live at Winfrith Newburgh where they share their cottage with a demented cat called Mr Pumfrey.

Ian Currie

The ever-changing moods and patterns of our skies have always fascinated Ian Currie. A spectacular thunderstorm over south east England on the 5th September 1958 and the prolonged deep winter snows 1962/63 were childhood memories that have never faded. Indeed his first weather station, a Christmas present, had only just been set up when it was buried by deep snow on Boxing Day 1962.

Sharing his interest with others has been a feature of Ian's life. He writes a weekly weather column for a number of newspapers including the *Surrey Mirror*, *Epsom Herald*, *Sutton Herald* and *Crawley News*. He successfully forecast the 1987 October storm for the *Surrey Mirror*. Ian helped to create the County Weather Book series starting with Surrey in 1990 and has written a number of other books including one about the Great Thames's Frost Fairs.

Ian has a weekly Weather Show on Telewest's Cable 17 TV channel and also a regular slot on BBC Southern Counties Radio. He is a freelance weatherman providing a variety of weather information for individuals and companies. Ian also gives over 200 talks a year to various groups, schools and societies. He is a Fellow of the Royal Meteorological Society and is on the Editorial Board of their weather magazine. He also helps to run the Climatological Observers Link, a group founded in 1970 for anyone interested in the weather.

A graduate in Earth Science and Geography, Ian is married with two boys and lives in Coulsdon, Surrey.

BOOKS available from Frosted Earth.

The Surrey Weather Book   ISBN 0-9516710-6-5   **£9.95.**
By Ian Currie and Mark Davison 1996 edition.

The Hampshire and Isle of Wight Weather Book   ISBN 1-872337-20-1   **£9.95**

The Berkshire Weather Book   ISBN 1-872337-48-1   **£9.95***

The Norfolk and Suffolk Weather Book   ISBN 1-872337-99-6   **£9.95***

The Sussex Weather Book   ISBN 1-872337-13-9 New Ed.   **£10.99***

The Kent Weather Book   ISBN 1-872 337-85-6 New Ed.   **£10.99***

Essex Weather currently out of print.

Red Sky at Night- Weather Sayings for all Seasons.   ISBN 0-9516710-2-2   **£4.95**
By Ian Currie

I Spy Weather published by Michelin 1-85671-131-5   **£1.25**
By Ian Currie

London's Hurricane   ISBN 0-9513019-3-4   **£4.95***
By Ian Currie and Mark Davison

Surrey in the Hurricane   ISBN 0-9513019-2-6   **£8.50**
By Ian Currie and Mark Davison

Surrey in the Sixties   ISBN 0-9516710-4-9   **£9.95**
By Ian Currie and Mark Davison

Surrey in the Seventies   ISBN 0-9516710-7-3   **£9.95**
By Ian Currie and Mark Davison

Frost, Freezes and Fairs   ISBN 0-9516710-8-1   **£8.95**
by Ian Currie

Hook Remembered   ISBN 0-9516710-9-X   **£9.95**
By Mark Davison

Surrey Street Croydon, A Stall Story.   ISBN 0-9516710-5-7   **£9.95**
By Vivien Lovett

* published by Froglets Publications.